C000153314

MOON LANDINGS
DID NASA LIE?

MOON LANDINGS
DID NASA LIE?

Philippe Lheureux

Carnot USA Books
22 West 19th Street, 5th Floor
New York, NY 10011

Copyright © 2003 by Carnot USA Books. All rights reserved. Except for brief passages quoted in a newspaper, magazine, radio, or television review, no part of this book may be reproduced in any form or by any means, electronic or mechanical, including photocopying and recording, or by any information storage and retrieval system, without permission in writing from the Publisher.

First edition
Originally published as *Lumieres sur la lune*
Translated and adapted by Tom Clegg by Editions Carnot, Chatou, France

Cover design by Priya Kale
Book design by Sharon Lewis
Printed in the United States of America

Library of Congress Cataloguing-in-Publication Data

Lheureux, Philippe.
    [Lumieres sur la lune. English]
    Moon Landings: did NASA lie to us? / Philippe Lheureux.
        p. cm.
    ISBN 1-59209-041-9 (pbk. : alk. paper)
1. Space flight to the moon.   2. Lunar bases.   3. United States.
National Aeronautics and Space Administration.
4. Truthfulness and falsehood. I. Title.
    TL799.M6 L4413 2003
    629.45'4'0973—dc21   2003005781

Published by:

Carnot USA Books, Inc.
22 West 19th Street, 5th Floor
New York, NY 10011
www.carnotbooks.com

212-255-6505
Email: sales@carnot.fr

To my mother, gone to join the stars

TABLE OF CONTENTS

Moon Landings

Chapter One

The Apollo Missions

Introduction

July 21, 1969. Everyone remembers Neil Armstrong's haunting declaration as he set foot on the lunar surface:

That's one small step for man,
One giant leap for mankind.

It was a perfect phrase—the continuing debate as to its spontaneity notwithstanding—because, at that moment, science fiction had become reality, the frontiers of the imagination had been expanded—science had just given us the Moon! It was a spectacular event, even better than the Super Bowl or a World Cup soccer final, because in this case there was no loser—the entire human race had won!

This historic mission was known as Apollo 11. It was soon followed by Apollo missions 12 through 17. With the exception of Apollo 13, which turned back following the explosion of an oxygen tank, the subsequent Moon landings were all reported as successful. As evidence, approximately 382 kg. (820 lbs.) of lunar material was brought back to Earth between the years 1969 and 1972.

And afterwards?

Strange as it may seem, it was the Soviets who continued to send rockets to the Moon. In 1974, Luna 22 was sent in lunar orbit, and tragically, Luna 23 crashed onto the Moon's surface.

In 1976, four years after the last Apollo mission, Luna 24, an unmanned Russian probe, successfully landed on the Sea of Crises and brought back to Earth 170 g. of samples from the lunar surface.

Strange, isn't it? Spending billions of rubles to recover 170 g. of lunar dust when the Americans already had multiples of this amount in their collection. Surely the Soviets had good reason for such an undertaking. Had the Americans been so stingy that they refused to give Russian scientists even 200 g. of samples out of the 382 kg. they had collected? Or did the Russians have cause to doubt the origin of the samples they had been given? The order of these events certainly raises some questions!

If the Russians were skeptical, they were not alone. Indeed, although it is not widely known, well before the time of the final Apollo mission, certain American media sources were already circulating rumors that the photographs from previous missions had been faked and that man had never actually set foot on the Moon.

The first part of this book is intended to take stock of this unsettling rumor. What evidence is it based on? Can it in any way be taken seriously? If so, it would seem that Neil Armstrong's famous step was indeed a giant leap—not into the future marked by progress, however, but one characterized by mass deception unprecedented in the history of scientific endeavor.

The Psychology of Doubt

To understand the underlying motivations of certain kinds of people, we must first come to accept that man has always seemed to be allergic to certainties. He prefers gray to black or white. If something is too black, he will add white, and, if it is too white, he will put in some black to stir things up. It is simply a part of human nature, evident in science as it is in politics. It is a phenomenon which we must come to terms with, even though it can be tiresome. Eventually, through this process, a balance inevitably establishes itself between an idea and its antithesis.

Here is another way of looking at this. Chinese philosophers say everything holds the seeds of its opposite.

Yin/Yang Symbol

If we accept this, then it is clear that opposition will eventually emerge to any prevailing idea, whether it be political or scientific in nature. It is therefore quite normal to find a certain number of people who resist even the most commonly held beliefs.

First Contact with the Rumor

The first person I ever heard raise doubts about the authenticity of the Moon landings was my Aunt Jeannine. She was a simple woman, who had always held some very conservative views. But when she told me that, in her opinion, the entire Apollo adventure had been produced in a movie studio, I burst out laughing! How could anyone be so dimwitted?

"And the rocks they brought back?" I demanded. "And the laser reflectors that were used to measure the distance from the Earth to the Moon?" I asked. "How did they get up there?" "It would be impossible to dupe the thousands of scientists who worked on the project," I insisted. "The hoax would have been leaked. The best proof that the Americans actually went to the Moon is that even the Russians have never denied it!" I raised all sorts of points, based on things I had heard from various sources, to try to show how ignorant she was on the subject.

It was all to no avail. The rocks could easily have been fabricated in a laboratory, she told me, and the reflectors deposited by unmanned probes. The scientists were all accomplices, since they worked for the army. As for the Russians, she did not trust them in times of war and still less in peacetime. There was just no convincing her! Each of us stuck to our guns, absolutely certain that the other was wrong. From then on, you can bet we always had plenty to talk about at family reunions.

Years passed. From time to time, I heard journalists on radio and television mocking people foolish enough to discredit the Apollo missions, and it intrigued me. What could possibly drive these naysayers to risk being ridiculed by their family, friends, and the press? After all, I had to acknowledge that someone had to be wholeheartedly convinced and seriously driven to bring this kind of ridicule upon themselves by publicly questioning what most consider to be one of the most glorious achievements in human history.

Cracks in the Walls of Science

For the sake of arguing, if we have been deceived, whose fault is it? It is the fault of people who use their scientific authority to manipulate and to misinform. After all, a scientific community which increasingly answers only to political and financial interests is in no position to reassure us.

Here are a few examples of what can happen when science is separated from conscience:

- When the first atomic bomb was detonated, scientists thought there was a chance that the chain reaction might destroy the entire planet, but they proceeded with the test nonetheless, at the order of politicians and the military.
- Later, when they knew full well the horrendous power of this type of weapon, they did not hesitate to unleash their creation upon the world.
- The American military even allowed their own troops to move into areas where atomic explosions had just taken place, in order to observe the effects of radiation on human beings.
- We are told that the dome of a nuclear reactor is capable of withstanding a plane crash, which is true—as long as the plane in question is a small two-seater, and it doesn't strike the cooling towers. In reality, most collisions would be so disastrous that air traffic is now entirely prohibited over nuclear reactors—although this has not prevented some planes from crashing less than two miles away.
- We are also informed that the electricity produced by nuclear power is "clean energy," which entirely ignores the problem of nuclear waste.

- In 1986, the citizens of France were told that the radioactive cloud from Chernobyl had stopped at the French border. A little later, the story had changed, and the French were told that even if the cloud had passed over their country, there was no danger because its radioactivity was less than that emitted by natural sources.
- Certain scientists have created meals from the meat of dead animals to be fed to livestock. Looks like we already have "soylent green" for cows![1]
- Medical science should have been able to cure cancer, but that has yet to happen! Moreover, new incurable diseases such as AIDS and mad cow disease have appeared. Perhaps part of the problem stems from the fact that, when diseases are too rare, they don't interest researchers because they have no commercial potential.

I will not cite other examples, but it would be quite surprising if the ones listed above fail to shake your faith in science to some degree. At the very least, one point should be clear: the simple fact that thousands of scientists participate in a research project does not guarantee that taxpayers and the general public will be told the truth. Why should things be any different in the conquest of space? What proof is there that we have really been told the truth?

The Shock of the Photos

I was speechless the day I found out that NASA's photos were being questioned. A colleague of mine brought me a copy of a magazine called *Facteur X*. On the cover was an eye-catching headline that could hardly have failed to grab my attention:

NASA CONSPIRACY
Moon Landing: the Faked Photos

Until then, I had heard people talk about this issue but had not yet experienced the shock of seeing the photos for myself. It was astonishing! Of course, the article itself was far from perfect. In fact, in many ways, it appeared to have been intended to discredit those who questioned the NASA version of the Apollo missions. For example, some of its criticisms could not be tested scientifically: a shadow that was too long, photos that had probably been retouched, a footprint in the wrong place.

Others involved gross errors of interpretation, such as the following:

These photos, like many of the shots taken during the Apollo missions, show a starless sky. Yet, since the Moon lacks any atmosphere, the stars should be visible, as has been confirmed to us by Maria Blyzinsky, conservator of astronomy at the Greenwich observatory in London.

But how could the stars be visible in the photos when the exposure time was too short to capture them?

Then there was the part about the flag being extended in a vacuum. Didn't everyone know that a horizontal extension bar ran along the top of the flag? Indeed, it was quite visible in some of the photos.

So these were the objections? Ridiculous! What a lack of credibility!

Disappointed by the ill-founded nature of an article that had not even been signed, I decided to try imagining what I would say if I were a journalist covering the story. Looking at the photo of astronaut Alan Bean with a test tube in his hand, I noticed certain anomalies that had not even been mentioned in the article:

- The spacesuit does not seem to be stretched by its internal pressure.
- The camera is not protected against the hazards of the lunar environment (270°F in the sunlight and –240°F in the shade, not to mention the harmful cosmic rays and the absence of atmospheric pressure). Why isn't it in a pressurized box?
- The stem of the reflector below the test tube does not appear to be attached to the upper section of the equipment.
- The astronaut is strongly lit while the lunar surface remains in darkness.

- The person taking the photo is lit from the front, while a companion is lit from the side.
- The lunar surface visible in the helmet is brighter than the one in the background.
- Why are the gloves black when the rest of the suit is white?

I pondered these issues but could not find a logical explanation. Then I went on to the other photos mentioned in the article.

It was like shooting fish in a barrel! It was obvious that certain photos had been retouched for patriotic and artistic reasons, but how could the anomalies in the photo of Alan Bean be explained? Had this really been taken on the Moon? Even if it had been shot in a studio, it seemed absurd to have made so many errors! A little compressed air would have sufficed to stretch the spacesuit and create the illusion of a vacuum.

Why did the article in *Facteur X* omit this? Was it an attempt to distract the reader from the real issues (a tactic commonly used in disinformation campaigns), or was I alone in seeing so many anomalies?

Thousands of scientists, including many from Russia, had seen these photos. Why were they silent about this? Was it not their responsibility as scientists to ask questions?

I found it difficult to believe that NASA had only been interested in the artistic aspect of the photographs! Were they afraid of ridicule? Had they been hypnotized by the event to the point of losing all of their critical faculties?

If they had tried to use the photographs scientifically, it would have been impossible to miss these errors. The entire situation was incomprehensible.

Enter the Internet

I decided to conduct my own research to see if I could find other anomalies or plausible explanations for the ones I had already uncovered. My first step was to visit the official NASA Web site[2] and download the pictures from the Apollo missions to study off-line.

I found so many puzzling things that I decided to publish the results of my investigation on the Web, in the hopes of obtaining some explanations from scientists. My site, *One Step Too Far,*[3] had been born! I have had about 5,000 visitors per month over two years and received a great deal of electronic mail. Some evenings, I received nearly 30 emails—with a peak of 147! About 98 percent of them were supportive, while the remaining two percent contained insults. Some Web surfers even accused me of altering the NASA photos myself—the cycle of skepticism never ends!

(By the way, I'd like to take the opportunity here to state that my goal has never been to criticize NASA. Whatever the truth and whatever their motives, NASA allowed us to dream and continues to do so. Without NASA, there could be no exploration of space.)

What I was most interested in, however, was hearing the reactions of scientists to the observations on my Web site. A close second was my interest in the psychology of doubt. Therefore, I deliberately took on the role of the Apollo missions' most vehement detractor, in order to provoke a reaction. One doesn't interfere with certain scientists over mere trifles, so I gave it all I had!

But the first people to react to my site were journalists. There were articles in Web 'zines (*DNA, Marchianne, Donquichotte, Yahoo Internet Life, Réponse Photo*, etc.) and television interviews in Belgium and France. Some, like *Donquichotte*, used the occasion of April Fools' Day to publish their articles. Fear of ridicule is not dead.

I thought my theories would be shot down from the start but to my astonishment, this was not the case. Here, for example, is an excerpt from the article in DNA:[4]

> *Among truly original personal Web pages, this one is...over the Moon! No doubt all of you remember the splendid photos that graced magazines during the Apollo years, the footprints, the astronaut in front of his module, etc. They were so beautiful and so well shot that the author of this home page started asking himself questions...and delivers to us his reflections and his doubts.*
>
> *And it's devastating! One can reasonably conclude, after examining his arguments, that these photos were at least retouched, if not actually shot in a studio right here on Earth. It takes up only one page, but what a page, well-reasoned and, above all, highly provocative in its implications.*

It seemed I was not the only one to spot anomalies in the photos of the Apollo missions. Journalists, along with ordinary citizens, had also seen them and didn't know what to make of them any more than I did. Indeed, if one believes the opinion poll presented at the bottom of my Web page, nearly 69 percent of those who participated believed that NASA had kept the real photos concealed.

General Results

Question: Do you think that NASA withheld the real photos?

Responses:	Votes	Percentages
YES	911	68.55
NO	248	18.66
Don't Know	170	12.79
Total	1329	100.00

Are we witnessing the dawning of a collective state of awareness? If so, it could be brutal.

The creation of *One Step Too Far* Web site and my participation in the *fr.sci.astronomie* newsgroup allowed me to glean some intelligent explanations from other Internet users. They are reproduced in this book in order to show that some of the anomalies observed were actually only errors in interpretation. Keep in mind, however, that I am not a "scientist," even if most of my remarks seem logical. So much the better for the Apollo missions.

Having said that, I must caution the reader against falling into the trap of lumping everything together. Just because one of my criticisms turns out to be faulty does not mean that I am mistaken about the others.

To end doubt, all the puzzles must be solved. Good luck!

A Nazi in NASA?

In reading some of the pages of this book, certain people might be tempted to accuse me of being a "revisionist." For them, calling into question the photos of the conquest of the

Moon is a crime equivalent to questioning the existence of concentration camps during the Second World War. One does not cast doubts with impunity upon an adventure which made millions of people dream.

As proof of this, witness the reaction of Philippe Vandel during the Canal+ television program. He concluded the report on me by saying:

But one should be careful; one starts by calling into question certain things, and then later one calls into question what happened between 1940 and 1944. Heider is good at that.

I answered him in the same tone:

But one should be careful; one starts by abandoning any critical sense concerning NASA's photos and then one forgets that Wernher Von Braun, the "father of the Moon rocket," was a Nazi engineer who openly worked for NASA without fear of prosecution.

In fact, at the end of the Second World War, the Americans reinstated German engineers who had worked on the V1 and V2 rockets and "offered" them "obligatory" employment in exchange for immunity. The Soviets did the same on their side and recovered material that had been left at various sites.[5]

According to many historians, certain scientists, like Wernher Von Braun, were not simply German engineers who had been requisitioned by the Nazis. They actively participated in the construction of the V1's and the V2's at the cost of 20,000 deportees' lives at the Dora prison camp. These prisoners were used unsparingly in the construction of underground factories.

To have offered these people immunity is certainly more serious than having retouched some photographs of the Moon or even to have faked a lunar mission.[6]

Moreover, the Nazis were gifted when it came to propaganda and the manipulation of crowds. Given that Wernher Von Braun was the boss of the Apollo missions, is it wise to place one's entire trust in NASA?

Analysis of the Photographs from the Apollo Missions

All of the photographs that follow were taken from *http://nssdc.gsfc.nasa.gov/planetary/lunar/apollo.html*. Certain pictures have been reframed, but none were modified to create anomalies deliberately. They are the official photographs released to the press between 1969 and 1973 that many of us could have seen in the paper or on television during that period.

Imagine yourself in a scientific police laboratory. Forget that thousands of scientists, journalists, and private individuals have examined these photos without finding anything abnormal. Look and try to see for yourself whether they are photos taken in a studio or real photographs that originated on the Moon. Ask yourself questions. Try to make the best use of your basic knowledge of physics and photography, and you'll be surprised at the results.

For those who have forgotten everything they once learned, I will go over the essential things you need to know about the Moon and in the field of photography before launching into the analysis of the pictures.

Lunar information

- The Moon has a mean diameter of 2,159 mi. compared to 7,922 mi. for the Earth, which makes the horizon much closer than our planet.
- As an indication of what this means, eyes that are 5 ft. 6 in. above the ground and looking out at the sea on Earth will see the horizon at a distance of 2.83 mi. On the Moon, the horizon would only be 1.51 mi. away.
- Lunar gravity is only 1/6 of that on Earth, which means that an astronaut in a spacesuit weighing 420 lbs. on Earth would only weigh 70 lbs. on the Moon.
- The Moon possesses no atmosphere, and the vacuum there is greater than the best vacuum that could be attained in a terrestrial laboratory.
- The absence of atmosphere causes the enormous range of temperatures observed at its surface: from +270°F in the sunlight to –240°F in the shade.
- The lunar surface is unprotected from all the harmful radiation that pours from the Sun (X rays, ultraviolet, infrared, solar, wind). It can also receive micro-meteorite shows.
- The solar wind is a wind of particles (protons, neutrons, electrons) that has nothing to do with terrestrial wind. It would be pointless to rely on it to explain a floating flag in a vacuum. (For that matter, NASA fixed a horizontal bar to the upper part of its mast to keep the American flag spread out.)
- For over 3.5 billion years, the Moon underwent a constant bombardment of meteors. This resulted in numerous visible craters and produced surface erosion. The regolith, a

coating of loose debris that comes from the physical fragmentation of the underlying rock, measures between three ft. and 30 ft. thick depending on the location, and covers the lunar relief. The permanent action of micro-meteorites as well as the temperature variations between day and night contributes to the erosion of the Moon and the creation of a layer of fine dust at the surface.

• There is no water in liquid form on the Moon. The samples brought back by the astronauts do not contain water molecules. On the other hand, in 1999, the American Lunar Prospector probe detected water at the South Pole in the form of ice. This probably came from the remnants of a comet.

• The Moon's albedo[7] is very weak: only 8.3 percent of the Sun's light is reflected by the lunar surface. The Moon turns itself so that it always presents the same face to the Earth. In fact, due to a slight oscillation, 59 percent of its surface can be seen from our planet.

• It is impossible to see an astronaut on the Moon from Earth, because the resolution of the best terrestrial telescope is only 600 ft. Only the Very Large Telescope (VLT) being built in Chile could theoretically permit viewing of the traces left by different lunar missions (but the telescope would still have to be aimed at them).

Photographic Information

A photographer's worst enemies are:

• Heat—If the temperature goes above +122°F, it accelerates chemical reactions in the gelatin, dilates the metallic parts of the camera, overheats the electronics, and causes the photo lenses to detach.

- X Rays—They can fog the film (and harm the photographer).
- Humidity—This is linked to condensation which can mist over the lens and alter the gelatin in the film.
- Ultraviolet rays—They alter the representation of color as well as the exposure time.
- Extreme cold—This renders the batteries in exposure meters unusable, makes film brittle, and contracts metallic parts.
- Dust
- Shocks
- Vacuum (on the Moon)—If the camera and lens cases have not been provided with holes for air to escape, the internal pressure of 14 lbs. per square in. risks damage to both the camera and the lens.
- When taking pictures, exposure meters balk at high contrasts and contre-jour shots. They also react badly to ultraviolet rays in large quantity and electromagnetic disturbances.
- On Earth, when unsure of the exposure, one can resort to "bracketing," that is to say, taking numerous photos of the same scene, gradually increasing the aperture to be sure of getting one with the correct exposure.
- Some dim objects, like stars, need a longer exposure time to register on the negative. That is the reason for their failure to appear on the astronauts' photos.
- The depth of field is the zone in which the objects in the photo remain in focus. It depends on the focal length and the aperture employed.

• A wide-angle lens is one which has a wider field of vision than the naked eye; it distorts perspectives by making the background seem more distant. A telephoto lens is one whose field of vision is more reduced than the naked eye; it enlarges objects and has a tendency to squash perspectives.

The Photographs in Question

NASA Photograph AS11-40-5877 (Apollo 11 mission)
This is a shot of the footprint made by Buzz Aldrin in order to study the nature of the lunar surface.

Let us recall Neil Armstrong's words: "That's one small step for man, one giant leap for mankind," and look more closely at what this footprint suggests 30 years later.

Description

The lunar surface seems to be composed of materials of various granular sizes (fine dusts, grains of sand, and small pebbles). There seems to be a crust at the surface (center right of the photo).

The print is deep. The grooves in the sole have left a clear imprint. The surface surrounding the footprint seems to have been compressed laterally judging by the bulges. The withdrawal of the foot has dislocated some of the groove prints, but they have retained their shape without collapsing. On the left-hand side of the photograph, a small block rests precariously on a groove.

Critical Analysis

I could have obtained the same kind of footprint on Earth by walking across clay, but surely not on the Moon unless there is water there in liquid form. Lunar Prospector, the most recent American probe, found water at the South Pole in the form of ice but nothing that would result in such cohesion of grains.

What is shocking is not the fact that the grooves of the sole are perfectly molded and retain their shape once the foot is removed. One could easily produce the same kind of print on Earth by walking in talcum or fine plaster. No, the most shocking thing is that certain imprints have dislocated without collapsing as one would have expected if they had been constituted by the dust of dry rock. A groove imprint (to the left of the photo) has broken and settled precariously. How could a small block constituted from the powder of anhydrous rock hold this position without collapsing?

NASA photograph AS11-40-5877 (enlargement)

And what should be made of the depth of the footprint? On the Moon, an astronaut only weighs 1/6 of his terrestrial weight. Consequently, I was expecting a footprint similar to what might be left in fine dry sand, that is, much less distinct. For these reasons, I found this photograph surprising to say the least. It completely contradicts what we have learned so far about the surface of the Moon, yet scarcely anybody appears to be shocked.

Elements of Scientific Responses

—On February 22, 2000, during the *Nulle part ailleurs*[8] television program on the French Canal + network, Philippe Vandel broadcast an interview in his 8:05 p.m. time slot. I had pre-recorded the show from home. The interview was followed by a response from André Brahic, a noted astrophysicist, who commented on the footprint.

Screen photograph of André Brahic carried out taken by a Web surfer during the broadcast

Here are segments from the broadcast:
Indeed yes, if you walked on clay, you would get a

similar picture, but that could also happen in other circumstances. On the Moon, what is going on?

Firstly, the gravity isn't the same. Secondly, there's no air, which means that this sort of dust, a little like sand on the beach, is very different from what we have on Earth because here molecules of air interpose themselves between the grains of sand on the ground when you walk, which makes it able to flow more easily. There you have no air, which means it's stickier in a way and that's what causes these traces.

And thus I see this boy who is pleasant, who asks the right questions, and the advice I would like to give him is this: that he should continue to ask himself questions, that he continue to be curious, that he continue to raise doubts about things but that he not draw conclusions too hastily.

In fact, for André Brahic and other scientists, the difference in gravity compared to Earth and the vacuum provided a sufficient explanation for the astonishing cohesion of the grains.

I disagreed. One-sixth of terrestrial gravity is still enough of a force to attract matter towards the center of the Moon. A famous experiment carried out during the Apollo 15 mission demonstrated that a feather and a hammer released at the same time four ft. above the surface of the Moon fell at the same speed.

To be sure, the Moon's pull is weaker than Earth's, but it exists. The proof of this was that dust churned up by the Moon buggy fell just as fast on the lunar surface as sand would fall on Earth. This was due in part to the absence of atmosphere which prevented its suspension in the air.[9]

On Earth, when a vacuum is created (as in a suction cup), the atmospheric pressure will cause the two sides to adhere to one another. If another vacuum around the outside of a suction cup is created, it will unfasten itself because there is no more air pressure to keep it fastened.

So the vacuum did not in any way assure the cohesion of the grains because, since it was everywhere, there couldn't be any suction effect. Only the texture of the lunar dust could explain this cohesion. In that case, the surface of each grain must be constituted in a way similar to velcro or Lego pieces.

In fact, the study of the samples brought back by the astronauts suffices to establish the truth. The total of 840 lbs. of samples collected by the missions have allowed scientists to determine that the fine regolith was comprised of rocky fragments, minerals, scoria and glass beads. The latter are crystals or rocks that had melted during meteorite impacts. They are 15 percent to 50 percent of fine regolith. This surface is not conducive to granular cohesion.

Edwin Aldrin on the Moon—An the Ideal Contre-Jour Shot

NASA Photograph AS-11-40-5903 (Apollo 11 mission)

Description

In this picture, Edwin Aldrin is almost lit in contre-jour and yet the smallest details of his spacesuit (the folds and hollows of the fabric) are perfectly visible. The luminosity is greater to the right of the photo behind the astronaut than in the landscape of the background.

There is a band of stronger lighting visible in the helmet visor and which follows the direction of Aldrin's shadow. In contrast, his shadow is completely black and erases any details of the lunar surface.

Neil Armstrong is located in front of Aldrin taking the picture. The LM is situated to the right of the photo in front of Edwin Aldrin.

Critical Analysis

The astronauts' photography equipment did not include a flash to remove shadows (the "fill in" effect). Moreover, if there had been a flash, it would be reflected in the helmet visor, because the astronaut who took the photograph is visible. The same would apply to an eventual projector fixed to the LM.

The lens of the camera used on the Moon was a 60mm Zeiss Biogon with a maximum aperture of 5.6. With a shutter speed better than 1/60th of a second[10] and 125 ISO film, it could not have let enough light pass to expose the areas in the shade correctly.

The fact that the lunar landscape visible in the background is much darker than the ground just behind the astronaut suggests it was taken in contre-jour. Except for a studio production with projectors and well-placed lights, there is no plausible explanation because, on the Moon, there are no clouds to block the sunlight.

(Just between you and me, if you went to the Moon, would you have taken your photographs in contre-jour or with the sun at your back? I myself would have opted for the second solution, in order to ensure myself the maximum chance of success. The first technique one learns in photography is precisely how to avoid contre-jour shots.)

Another astounding thing is that the spacesuit has so many folds and hollows. Now, what happens to air imprisoned in a hermetic balloon when the external pressure diminishes? It dilates, and the balloon swells.

Since the suit was put on inside the LM under atmospheric pressure, the air contained inside it would have dilated because of the lunar vacuum. Given the internal pressure, the fabric of the spacesuit should have been stretched. It is obvious that the suit was designed to resist this dilation, but that does not explain the reason for the folds and hollows in the tissue.

Verification of whether this internal tension of the suit hinders the bend of the arms and legs could take place on Earth. All you would have had to do is put on the suit and pressurize it to twice the atmospheric pressure in order to replicate what happens on the Moon.

I also wonder about the weatherproofing used in the clothing. The suits had to have been designed to:
- Prevent respiration from fogging the helmet visor
- Maintain a tolerable temperature inside the suit
- Enable the skin to breathe
- Prevent breathing of too cold air, or on the contrary, prevent explosions of the pressurized bottles due to excessive heat

Since outside temperatures on the Moon reach 270 degrees F. in the sun and –240 degrees F. in the shade, the photographs leave unanswered questions:

- Why aren't the gloves white when hands are among the human organs most sensitive to cold and heat and probably the most difficult in terms of climate control?
- How is protection against X Rays achieved?
- What level of X Ray reaches the lunar surface?
- Is it compatible with the need to take photographs without risking fogging the film?

Here is another photograph of Edwin Aldrin at the same place. Here, too, the shadows have been filled incorrectly and the solar lighting is punctual. There is also an absence of scraping around the foot of the LM. It has set itself gently on the ground without slipping in the dust.

NASA photograph AS11-40-5902 (Apollo 11 mission)

Elements of scientific responses

—During its program "Ça, alors"[11] on March 21, 2000, the Belgian television channel RTL TVI broadcast an interview carried out in my home by Luc Gilson, followed by a response by Marcello Coradini, a scientist working for the European Space Agency (ESA).

Here is Coradini's answer to a question:

It is true . . . there are zones that are not directly lit by the solar light and that in principle should remain totally in the shade. But it must also be remembered that the lunar surface reflects light and consequently, the part that isn't directly lit by the Sun is lit by the light that is reflected by the lunar surface.

Phillipe Lheureux

I still disagree with him. In this shot, the ground is flat, and the LM that could have reflected the solar light is situated on the wrong side of the astronaut to do so. Look closely at the left part of the backpack. All the details are clearly visible, and the helmet masks any eventual reflection from the LM. Remember the albedo of the lunar surface; you might as well be trying to fill in the shadows using a badly oriented piece of gray cardboard that only reflected 8.3 percent of the sunlight.

Out of a concern for objectivity, here are some other responses obtained within the newsgroup *fr.sci.astronomie*. They do not all emanate from scientists but denote another manner of seeing this data.

• The attenuation of the light stems from the nature of the

film, or the alteration of film due to the conditions when taking the shot.

- The photograph was deliberately retouched in the laboratory by NASA before its release to the press. The shadows were filled in by a longer exposure (the masking technique).
- The astronaut's suit was made of several different layers. The outer layer is not the one that resists pressure, so it is normal that it does not stretch.

Here is a photograph taken on Earth during the astronauts' training. It is easy to verify that there is no difference with respect to the folds.

NASA Photo AP11-69-H-698 (Apollo 11 Mission)

Phillipe Lheureux

Given the weight of their suits, the astronauts can be observed on Earth compensating for gravity by leaning forward and bending their legs slightly. To recreate lunar conditions, all that is needed is to remove the bottles from their backpacks.

In fact, the most astonishing thing is the way the astronauts walk on the Moon, taking gliding steps and crab walking. Why would an astronaut start to walk sideways on the Moon when he only weighs 65 lbs.?

A Controlled Slide

Astronaut Charles Duke beside the Moon buggy
NASA Photograph AS16-107-17446 (Apollo 16 mission)

Description

Here is a rear view of an astronaut next to the Moon buggy.

This time, the shadows falling on his suit are very black. There is a field of stones with tire tracks that turn 90 degrees after having passed over some big stones. A measuring instrument on a tripod stands on the field of stones.

Critical Analysis

Clearly, they are not good at centering shots at NASA. This nice photograph of a back stands little chance of being published in a photo magazine, except in the "rejects" column. Why not have waited until the astronaut turned before taking the picture?

However, the objective was surely to show us the tire tracks in order to underline the Moon buggies' rugged capabilities. So, let's look at them more closely.

It looks like drivers' licenses, like photography, may not be one of NASA's stronger points, unless they were trying to damage the lunar vehicle by rolling on stones. The astronauts, alone on the Moon, had to play it safe and limit their field of travel to six mi. around the LM. Thus, it is astonishing that they would have taken the risk of damaging their vehicle on the stones.

Judging by the numerous tire tracks, this patch of stones particularly interested them. The first big stone on the left has a "C" engraved on it. Where did this come from?

Most of the tire tracks have grooves, but, after the last big stone, they become smooth, as if the vehicle had been pulled along by hand. The turning circle is incredibly short. It almost makes a right angle. Moreover, the rear tires follow the same path as those in front. This buggy must be some vehicle!

Look also at the landscape in the background, beyond the

buggy. It becomes surprisingly blurry. With such luminosity and by stopping down to an aperture of f: 22, any one of us could surely have done better. Do not forget that the lens used was a super wide-angle; the photograph should thus be in focus from three ft. to infinity. Unless we have been presented with an assembly from two different photographs perhaps?

Those of you who taped video cassettes showing the movement of this vehicle on the Moon should look carefully at the dust thrown backwards by the wheels. It's amusing to see that this dust behaves like sand and, in the end, is not thrown up much higher than on Earth.

It would also be interesting to learn more about the problem of the buggy's batteries. How can they withstand the extreme temperatures on the Moon?

Dust raised by the buggy's wheels
NASA photograph S72-37002 (Apollo 16 mission)

Here, the cohesion of grains does not seem to come into play.

NASA Photograph S72-36970 (Apollo 16 mission)

The delicate equipment certainly seems to have been subjected to rough treatment. It is likely the buggy's antenna and camera were damaged.

Elements of Scientific Responses

—The Moon buggy has four wheels and an independent suspension that allows the rear wheels to follow the front wheels' tracks.

Alright. However, this option must have been exercised at just the right moment.

—There is no element to indicate the distance to the LM. If it was the end of the mission, the buggy could undergo a final test by riding over the stones.

It would have been more judicious to send it out roving without a driver. It could have transmitted pictures from beyond the zones explored by the astronauts.

—As far as the field depth is concerned, the camera lens was a 60 mm Zeiss Bigon with a maximum aperture of f: 5.6.

That means it is a super wide-angle lens and not very "luminous." The lenses used on Earth often go as low as f: 2.8 or even f: 1.8.

Remember that one of the characteristics of a wide-angle lens is that it has great depth of field. In general, at f: 5.6 the photograph is in focus from three ft. to infinity. For the background to become blurred just behind the buggy would have meant an aperture of f: 1.8.

The Mister Bean of the Apollo 12 Mission

Alan Bean
NASA Photograph AS12-49-7278 (Apollo 12 mission)

Description

The astronaut Alan Bean is lit from the side and holds a test-tube in his right hand. All the details of his spacesuit are clearly visible. The suit seems to cling to his skin in the area of the biceps. The camera is hooked to the front of his suit at the height of his thorax.

In his reflective visor, one can see plainly the astronaut taking the picture. The bright spot in the upper left-hand corner seems to be a reflection from a metallic part.

The lunar surface in the background does not reflect light, despite the intense lighting on the suit.

Critical Analysis

Once again, the contre-jour shot is ideal. The shadows are all filled in without the use of a flash. Surprisingly, the reflection in the helmet visor shows shadows that run in two different directions. But no matter how hard I look outside, I don't see two Suns. Even more astonishing, the astronaut taking the shot is lit from the front while facing someone lit in profile.

It is also important to note that the astronauts don't seem to take very good care of their photographic equipment. The camera does not seem particularly well-protected from the dust, the vacuum, the cold, the heat, or the X-ray and ultraviolet radiation. Remember that the temperature on the Moon can rise to 270 degrees F in full sunshine, and the surface receives all of the solar radiation without an atmospheric filter. Why is there no gold reflective foil wrapped around this camera when there is around the LM's landing pads and the cameras aboard the Moon buggy? The film and the lens risk being seriously damaged.

Moreover, what film can withstand a temperature range going from −240 degrees F to +270 degrees F. without any protection other than the camera case? If someone had asked me to design a camera adapted to lunar conditions, I would have put it in a pressurized protective case with temperature control like those used for depth photography underwater.

Yet, I have trouble believing that NASA faked all the photos for each mission because the astronauts could not take photographs correctly on the Moon. If NASA was capable of going there, they should certainly have been able to construct a camera which could withstand extreme conditions.

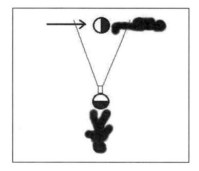

The arrow indicates the direction the sunlight is coming from. It is bright enough to light the side of the spacesuit but apparently not enough to light up the ground behind the astronaut. Here again, the background becomes blurry and darkens for no valid reason. What is more, the reflection in the astronaut's visor shows a lunar surface that is more luminous than that of the background!

Once again the spacesuit is sticking to the astronaut's skin rather than swelling due to the vacuum. The internal pressure of 14 lbs. per square in. does not seem to have prevented the astronaut from folding his arms easily.

The most improbable fact of all is that the lower part of the instrument the astronaut holds in his hand is not attached to the rest. That is going a bit too far.

Elements of Scientific Responses

Hasselblad Data Camera

—This is what the lunar photo equipment looked like. This is a modified version of the Hasselblad 500EL camera, utilized for photogrammetry shots at medium resolution during the Apollo and Skylab missions. The camera includes a glass network plate positioned immediately in front of the 70 mm film. The network plate places a system of cross hairs on each photo to facilitate its photogrammetric use. The camera weighs 3.1 lbs., the lenses are 60 mm Zeiss Biogon f : 5.6.

—Here is Arnaud Delaunay's comment on the subject:[12]

The film is not subjected to the same conditions as the

camera itself. For one thing, the change in temperature is not immediate. One doesn't go from −240 degrees F to +270 degrees F instantly by simply turning one's back. Try to remember your physics lessons or steal the schoolbooks of your children . . . Next, we're in a vacuum, remember? And what is one of the best thermal insulators? VACUUM. Because there's no heat conduction. That's by the way the very principle of thermos bottles. The camera heats due to its direct exposure to the sun, but the film is very well protected.

Philippe Lheureux

Here, it's a question of remaining in the range of + 120 degrees F to −50 degrees F. If the camera, whose film was loaded under atmospheric pressure, did not have a depressurization valve to empty air from the interior, then the air trapped inside would heat up due to contact with the camera case and damage the film. It would also exert strong pressure on the surrounding walls.

It should be pointed out that, if a vacuum is a good insulator, the metallic parts attached to the camera case to hold the shutter and film are not. One might also wonder what happens to the air trapped between the lenses when the astronaut goes out to shoot in a vacuum, and why the outside of the lens is painted black (a heat absorber) rather than white (which is not as absorbent).

In any case, the pictures below would seem to indicate that the camera's frontal position is not very ergonomic for handling the shovel or descending the LM's ladder. Why attach it to one side of the helmet? That would also have given it more protection if the astronaut fell.

About the Lighting of the Scene

Here is a study carried out by Bernard Lemoine and Jean-Luc Destombes from the Laboratoire de Physique des Lasers, Atomes et Molécules[13] at the University of Science and Technology in Lille, France.

The photo reproduces (with two bottles of milk and a Christmas tree ball) the apparent incoherence of the shadows that one observes by reflection in Alan Bean's visor photographed by Conrad (Apollo 12). This effect is simply due to the distortion of perspectives produced by a reflection on a spherical surface. It shows how the shadows from Bean's suit[14] are generously lit by the reflection of the suit worn by the astronaut taking the picture. That's how the best contre-jour shots were taken.

Philippe Lheureux

Bravo to these two scientists for being able to demonstrate, with a minimum of equipment, that this is an optical illusion linked to the spherical shape of the visors. Still, there is one shadow whose cause is yet to be explained. This is the one that meets the shadow of the astronaut taking the photo.

About the Test Tube

Here is Arnaud Delaunay's comment:

It is the Special Environmental Sample Container, a tool that was used until Apollo 17. The object of this instrument is to bring back samples in a vacuum of sorts. The utilization of the instrument is as follows: the astronaut removes the seal of the container in order to open it. Then, using a special instrument, he gathers the sample

and pours it into the container (in the photo, one can see that the container is full). Next, the astronaut takes the cover which, until then, has hung from the bottom of the container by a fine wire (which one can see on the right of the container's arm). Then he only has to spin the cover arm to seal up the container.

Philippe Lheureux

Personally, I don't see any wire in the photograph, and judging from this picture the center of gravity of the cover would have caused most of the stem to hang downwards. But let's allow for it to be a different model and for the cable to be too fine to be seen in the photograph.

James Irwin Salutes You.

James Irwin
NASA Photograph AS15-88-11866 (Apollo 15 mission)

Description

This scene is lit from the side. In it, astronaut James Irwin is saluting the American flag. The lunar buggy and the LM seen on the ground is much darker than the mountainous region visible in the background.

Critical Analysis

The sign reading "United States" on the contre-jour portion of the LM should have been in total blackness. Instead, it appears white.

Judging by the direction of the shadows of the LM and the astronaut, the imposing mountain behind the LM should be partially in the shade. Instead, its slopes seem entirely illuminated by the Sun.

The details of James Irwin's spacesuit should not be visible since he is almost in contre-jour.

And it is astonishing that NASA picked this place for a landing. What if the LM had landed on the mountain?

A close inspection of the lunar surface behind the astronaut clearly reveals the boundary with the mountain. The lunar sand in the foreground is darker than it is in the background even in parts where the astronauts have not walked. Its border with the lighter section is very sharp, almost as if the ground had been raked.

As shown on the next page, another photograph of the same place clearly shows the border between the two ground colors. In this photograph, there is a halo that could be dust in suspension. The problem is that dust cannot remain in suspension in a vacuum. It would instantly fall back to the ground. In all the photographs of the lunar landings at the NASA site, I have not found any taken that face an astronaut with the Sun behind the photographer. They are shot either in contre-jour or with the Sun to the side. Is that because of the risk that the real light source would be reflected by the astronaut's helmet?

NASA Photograph AS15-88-11863 (Apollo 15 mission)

Elements of Scientific Responses

—The mountain behind has a gentle slope. If the Sun had been high enough in the lunar sky, its rays would not have been blocked.

—It is obvious that the "United States" sign was deliberately filled in at the laboratory, but touching up a photograph to make a patriotic emblem more distinct does not mean the photo was taken in a studio.

—According to NASA, the mountain in the background is far away from the LM (about three mi.). They claim the shot used a zoom lens that squashed the relief.

Philippe Lheureux

Here is a shot of the same LM taken from the right of the preceding photo. More information is needed on whether the lens was wide-angle or zoom. While the LM is not as close to the neighboring mountains as it seemed in the first picture, the degree of difference is minimal in terms of the discrepancies at hand. A comparison of the distance to the LM's size proves that it is much less than three mi. (see the aerial view of the Apollo 15 mission below near the end of this chapter). If the mountains had really been that far from the LM, they would be emerging from the horizon line, which is not the case.

The LM in Contre-Jour

NASA Photograph AS14-66-9306 (Apollo 14 mission)

Description

In this shot, the LM of Apollo 14 is in full contre-jour. Although the Sun is hiding behind the LM, it is causing a reflection to interfere with the upper part of the photo.

Critical Analysis

Did NASA decide to waste film? What is the scientific interest of such a photograph? To present us with a contre-jour shot whose shadows have been skillfully filled in without using a flash is already an exploit, but with the reflection of the Sun shining straight into the lens, it is truly miraculous.

Hasselblad really performed a technical feat with its equipment. With a shutter speed better than 1/60th of a second[15] and film of 125 ISO, it could not let enough light pass to expose the images in the shade correctly.

As for the LM's size, the upper part must be big enough to carry two astronauts in their suits, plus their oxygen reserves, food, the samples gathered, and the necessary fuel for the return flight. It seems a little small to perform its return function. I would be curious to see what would happen if one did the calculations all over again.

How much fuel is needed to free the LM from the Moon's attraction (only 1/6th of the Earth's gravity)? Is this amount of fuel really compatible with the size of the LM's tanks? I have not even mentioned the problems of balancing the craft in liftoff and again in landing, when the form is different.

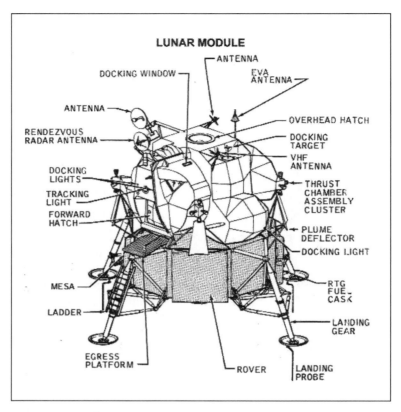

LUNAR MODULE

ANTENNA

DOCKING WINDOW

EVA ANTENNA

ANTENNA

OVERHEAD HATCH

RENDEZVOUS RADAR ANTENNA

DOCKING TARGET

VHF ANTENNA

DOCKING LIGHTS

THRUST CHAMBER ASSEMBLY CLUSTER

TRACKING LIGHT

FORWARD HATCH

PLUME DEFLECTOR

DOCKING LIGHT

MESA

RTG FUEL CASK

LADDER

LANDING GEAR

EGRESS PLATFORM

ROVER

LANDING PROBE

Elements of Scientific Responses

—None were received for this section. Plans of the LM speak for themselves.

—The LM is piloted like a combat tank, if the sizes of the viewing ports are any indication. Balancing during the descent eats into fuel reserves needed for the return flight because there are no ejection nozzles in the lower part.

—It does not seem to be an easy device to pilot. And it is not clear how the astronauts perform the rendezvous during the

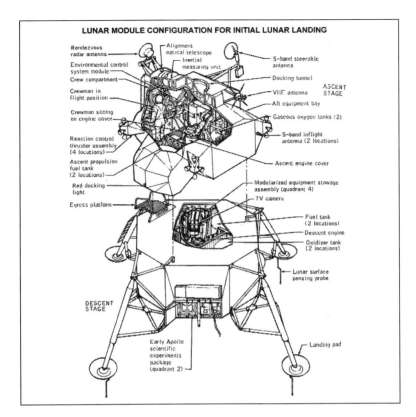

LUNAR MODULE CONFIGURATION FOR INITIAL LUNAR LANDING

return with the capsule remaining in orbit. How can the docking occur at the top of the LM if the standing position of the pilot prevents him or her from looking through the docking window?

—No decompression lock is visible. This means that, when the astronaut leaves, it is necessary to depressurize the entire cabin.

—For the return, the astronaut who is not the pilot sits on the surface of the ascent engine. That's what one might call "having your fanny warmed."

—Would you have risked your life in this kind of machine? Not I.

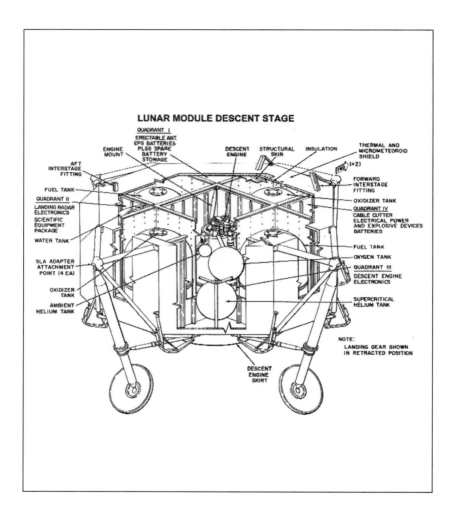

LUNAR MODULE DESCENT STAGE

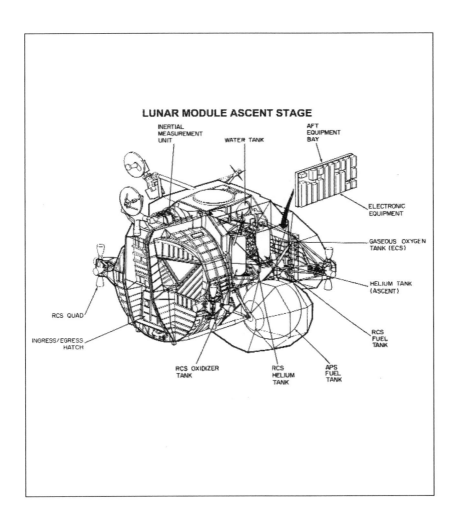

LUNAR MODULE ASCENT STAGE

A Very Close Horizon

NASA Photograph AS11-40-5962 (Apollo 11 mission)

Description

Here is the LM of Apollo 11 against a black background. The shadow of the astronaut taking the photograph and the shadow of the LM seem to converge at the same vanishing point. The horizon seems to pass just behind the LM.

Critical Analysis

At first, I thought the convergence of the shadows in this photograph was proof of the use of artificial lighting in the scene. My reasoning was as follows: since the Sun is a luminous point located 90 million mi. away, and its rays diverge the further they travel, a straight line from the astronaut's shadow should intersect with the LM's shadow at the Sun.

Elements of Scientific Responses

—It is of course an optical illusion, not a cinema backdrop.

—The moon has an average diameter of 2,159 mi. compared to Earth's 7,922 mi., which makes the horizon much closer than on our planet. To demonstrate the effects of this difference, on Earth, eyes that are situated five ft. six in. above the ground will see the horizon at a distance of 2.83 mi. when they look out to sea, but, on the Moon, they will see it 1.51 mi. away.

—In this photo, the terrain is flat, and our senses are tricked because they refer to known conditions on Earth.

Philippe Lheureux

On the Moon the horizon is closer, but this seems extremely close.

Here is another photo of Apollo 11's LM showing the proximity of the horizon.

Aldrin after the deployment of a scientific experiment package.
NASA Photograph AS11-40-5948 (Apollo 11 mission)

I have to thank Mario Hebert, a Canadian Web surfer for taking the time to demonstrate that my doubts were groundless and that the convergence I noticed was only an optical illusion caused by the effect of perspective.[16] It is also noteworthy that there is no trace of footprints between the LM and the astronaut taking the photograph, as if he or she had deliberately taken a circular route to avoid taking a picture of their footprints.

Here's what Hebert reported:

The important implication in the matter we are considering is that the shadow of the astronaut photographer on the real lunar surface is, without question, going in exactly the same direction as the LM.

For the LM, obviously, only the shadow's length varies but not its orientation because it is bigger than the astronaut's.

The other thing to notice is that the closer the shadow to the camera lens, the straighter it seems. This is the effect of an optical illusion.

In real life (on the Moon), all the shadows are parallel on the ground, as the picture above shows, but if one observes this result on a two-dimensional support such as a photograph or a picture on a computer screen, perspective will play a role and give us the result observed above. The photograph covers an angle exactly in the horizontal and vertical directions.

I repeat that, here, the light source is comparable to the Sun, situated 90 million mi. behind. Our salutations, then, to the luckiest of photographers who, 30 years ago, could peacefully take a photograph in all its imperfections, in the calm and tranquility of the lunar surface." [17]

Philippe Lheureux

To be sure of this point, a computer simulation of the lunar horizon is required. For those who, like myself, doubted at the beginning that the convergent shadows could be caused by the Sun, here are the digital pictures created by Mario Hebert. The cylinder stands in for the LM.

Philippe Lheureux

It would have been easy to pass over this reply in silence when writing this book, but the aim is not to dupe readers. Winning a battle does not mean the war is won, too. The fact that one remark has found a plausible explanation does not mean that all the criticisms expressed in this book will find one. Mario Hebert's study demonstrates that the convergence of shadows was normal. Not that the photograph had in fact been taken on the Moon.

The Earth as Seen from the Moon

NASA Photograph 1S17-137-20910 (Apollo 17 mission)

Description

A big granular rock in the foreground. There are fissures in the rock as well as stria. Over the rock, the Earth stands out against a black backdrop.

Critical Analysis

The background showing the lunar surface closely resembles an aerial view of the Moon. Nevertheless, I have trouble believing that this rock is at the summit of a mountain. Also, the Moon is covered by a layer of dust about two in. thick. Why are there no traces of it on the rock in the foreground?

Unfortunately, the astronaut did not take the time to place an object of known dimensions on the rock to give some idea of its relative size. A simple hammer would have sufficed.

The Earth, which should appear 3.67 times the diameter of the Moon as seen from our world, seems very small and quite low on the horizon. Compare its size to the photo that follows, which shows the Earth as seen from a lunar orbit.

NASA Photo AS11-44-6549

This photograph covers a great portion of the Moon, and the Earth seems enormous here compared to the one taken at the surface. Is this an optical illusion or a poor fake?

As far as the external appearance of the rock is concerned, the presence of stria is puzzling, but there are not enough elements to say more. Normally, it is impossible for it to be a sedimentary rock.

Elements of Scientific Responses
—The photo taken from the Moon was shot with a wide-angle lens, judging by the great depth of field. Wide-angle lenses tend to enlarge the foreground and reduce the background.

Philippe Lheureux
Here are the texts that accompany the photos on NASA's site. It should be noted that the two photos belong to different missions. Unfortunately, there is no mention of the lenses used in taking the shots. Too bad.

• For the Earth seen from the lunar surface:
NASA Photo ID: AS17-137-20910

File Name:	*10075958.jpg*
Film Type:	*70 mm Date Taken: 12/12/72*
Title:	*View of boulder photographed during second Apollo 17 EVA*
Description:	*View of boulder at Station 2 (Amundsen Crater, photographed during second Apollo 17 extravehicular activity (EVA-2). The earth can be seen directly above the boulder in the lunar sky.*

Subject terms:
Apollo 17 Flight
Apollo Project
Extravehicular Activity

Lunar Photography
Lunar Rocks
Lunar Surface

• *For the Earth seen from the capsule in orbit:*

NASA Photo ID:	*AS11-44-6549*
File Name:	*10075247.jpg*
Film Type:	*70 mm Date Taken: 07/16/69*
Title:	*View of Earth rising over Moon's horizon taken from Apollo 11 spacecraft*
Description:	*This view of the Earth rising over the Moon's horizon was taken from the Apollo 11 spacecraft. The lunar terrain pictured is in the area of Smuth's Sea on the nearside. Coordinates of the center of the terrain are 85 degrees east longitude and three degrees north latitude.*

Subject terms:
Apollo 11
Apollo Project
Earth (Planet)
Earth Observations (from space)
Horizon
Lunar Surface
Lunar Topography
Moon
Onboard Activities
Photography

The Absence of Dust on Lunar Rocks

NASA Photograph AS17-145-22157 (Apollo 17 mission)

Description

The astronaut Schmitt gathering samples of lunar soil.

Critical Analysis

The surface of the Moon is covered in a layer of dust, called the "regolith," whose thickness varies from a few inches to many feet. The meteoritic bombardment crumbled the lunar crust and formed this layer of debris, which becomes finer the closer one approaches the surface. Why is this dust, the fruit of meteoritic strikes, not deposited on the lunar rocks? On Earth, the wind and the rain sweep away dust from rocks, but, on the Moon, there is no atmosphere and thus no wind or rain.

Elements of Scientific Responses

—The Moon is constantly bombarded by atomic nuclei released by the Sun, or electrons ejected into space that ionize its surface. This phenomenon takes place on the sunlit surfaces of the ground and the rocks, only to disappear during the lunar night. Everyone knows that bodies bearing identical electric charges repel one another. You may have seen, in electrostatic experiments, particles violently repelling one another when they are charged the same way. The dust on the Moon's surface is very light and has a relatively large surface area. Therefore, it is normal that the sunlit surfaces of rock, which are charged positively by ejecting electrons, chase away the dust particles on its surface. In the long run, very weak movements suffice to do this so that there is no longer anything on the rock, including relatively heavy grains. Because it is less directly exposed to various types of solar radiation, the lower part of the rock acquires less of a charge and attracts particles by electrostatic differential. As a side note, this provides a means of knowing what height a small grain of dust is capable of jumping to under the effect of electric repulsion.

—The astronauts were able to observe a strange phenomenon while on the Moon—dust shining over the surface, in the sunlight on the horizon. This dust is held in suspension by the phenomenon of electrostatic levitation. It has been calculated that even the very smallest grains acquire enough velocity to escape the pull of lunar gravitation, and it's been observed that the Moon is followed in its orbit by a tail of dust from its surface.

Philippe Lheureux

It is correct that clouds of dust have been observed on the Moon.[18] But if this were due to the Sun, such observations would not be local. As the Sun began to shine on the lunar surface, the dust would rise in suspension and would prevent any decent photos from being taken on the Moon.

The jets of dust could very well be caused by the release of gases through fissures in the lunar crust or, worse still, by what is described in Chapter Three.

It should be noted that any suspended dust falls back to the surface. Why doesn't it fall back on the rocks?

Takeoff of Apollo 17's LM

Here are two pictures taken from the film.

NASA Photograph S72-55422 (Apollo 17 mission)

Description

The previous photo shows the ignition of an engine creating a big spray of sparks followed by a jet of gas under pressure that disappears quickly.

NASA Photograph S72-55421 (Apollo 17 mission)

Description

This is the ascent of the LM, climbing all alone in the vacuum, without any visible flame from the engine. The camera that stayed on the lunar vehicle did a reverse zoom, following it to a point located very high in space.

Critical Analysis

These video pictures are supposed to have been taken during the re-launch of the LM from the Apollo 17 mission (the last one). For those who have been lucky enough to see the film, it is the camera that remained onboard the lunar vehicle that filmed the scene.

There is a reverse zoom and a pan of the LM's nearly vertical ascent, all of it piloted from Earth. Due to the time lag in signals, it was a technical exploit.

NASA Photograph S69-39011 (Apollo 11 mission)

The engine ignition leads to a big spray of sparks that propagate astonishingly well in the vacuum. The return module detaches itself. A little jet of gas under pressure can be seen but then nothing is visible—no gas and no flame. The LM climbs all on its own into space as if it is lifted by a rope. It must be a magical fuel that burns without making flames and produces a transparent gas. Even the artists working for NASA were unaware of this type of fuel, judging from their paintings.

This is only a painting, but everything is there, even the

"United States" sign that glows in the dark. The shadows visible on the LM totally contradict those of the landscape in the background. It is astonishing that artists would make such mistakes with shadows.

NASA Photograph S69-39335 (Apollo 11 mission)

The fuel used was the same during arrival and return. At least, that is what NASA tells us on its Web site. Even the artists knew. So, why did the LM from Apollo 17 take off without any flame?

Elements of Scientific Responses

—Here is an email from a Web visitor who claims to have worked on the Ariane rocket:

If I may venture a small comment, in space there is no air. So one would need to furnish:

1) fuel

2) oxidizer

That would have been too heavy for the lunar module. They remedied this problem of excess load by propelling the module, after its takeoff, thanks to gas "identical" to what one finds in any aerosol can (shaving cream, whipped cream). That explains why one cannot see anything.

Philippe Lheureux

We are out of luck here. By referring to LM plans reprinted above, it is clear that the engine on the return module is fed both fuel and oxidizer. In fact, according to NASA, it uses the same type of fuel during both descent and ascent.

The most plausible explanation is that the mixture obtained creates a flame that is not very visible or that is one difficult to capture on film.[19] It is N204/UDMH. The oxidizer (nitrogen peroxide) and the fuel (unsymmetrical dimethyl hydrazine or UDMH) are hypergolic ergols, meaning they burst into flame spontaneously upon contact with one another. They are insensitive to shocks. This combination is also of an extreme purity (98-99 percent) and thus produces no particles that would make the engine's exhaust visible. There's nothing magical about all that.

—Regarding the perfect pan of the LM by the camera on the ground, Marcello Coradini of the ESA gave an explanation that left me baffled because it completely contradicted what other experts have reported.

Here is an excerpt from the video of *"Ça alors"*[20] shown on March 21, 2000 on the Belgian RTL TVI channel:

Marcello Coradini—

It is a very simple thing. The camera is in a very contrasted situation, the lunar surface being very clear, and a source of heat and light like the engine of the lunar model is very easy to follow. It only requires a little photoelectric cell.

Philippe Lheureux

Documentaries about the Moon race give a different version. They claim the camera remaining on the Moon buggy was piloted from Earth by NASA technicians. This explains the reverse zoom, which would have been difficult to perform with a photoelectric cell.

When I suggest that the problem comes from the fact that the flame is invisible, I am told that a source of heat and light like the LM engine is easy to follow. It is enough to make you believe that the engine only emits in infrared. On the other hand, the spray of sparks in a vacuum—without oxygen—is difficult to manage unless the expelled product contained its own oxidizer and was constituted by white-hot metal.

—Another explanation received by email:

If there aren't more flames, it's because the motor is extinguished. It just did a long enough burn to give the impulse needed to permit the LM to liberate itself from the Moon's attraction.

Philippe Lheureux

Normally, it is at takeoff that the push must be the strongest and the most sustained. To extinguish the engine at that point would be the best way never to see Earth again.

Family Photo

NASA Photograph AS16-117-18841 (Apollo 16 mission)

Description

Here, the astronaut is acknowledging his wife and children by leaving a family photo on the lunar surface. What could be more human than to want to leave an eternal trace of one's stay on the Moon?

Critical Analysis

The astronaut has taken care to place the photo of his family in a plastic bag. It is unclear why, unless he heard that rain was in the forecast on the Moon.

If the bag was hermetically sealed during the exit from the LM, the internal atmospheric pressure would have caused it to burst or at least become swollen once it was in contact with a vacuum.

But let us assume that the air inside escaped during depressurization. Why then, does the plastic look as if the pressure in the bag was below that on the exterior?

And what can be said about placing plastic from the Apollo 16 era on a surface whose temperature in full sunshine is in the neighborhood of 270° F? How could it successfully withstand such heat? Bear in mind that the lunar regolith only reflects eight percent of the solar light and absorbs a maximum amount of infrared rays.

Personally, if I left a photo of my family on the Moon, I would have sheltered it from the sunlight by hanging it to the stake of an experiment or in the buggy. Throwing a photo on the ground seems strange.

While on the subject, the astronauts must have suffered from hot feet.

Elements of a Scientific Explanation

—The astronaut must have taken the photo very quickly, since the plastic did not have time to melt.

Phillipe Lheureux

Recreating the experiment will determine the truth:
Materials—A photograph which is not important to you, a plastic sandwich bag, an old frying pan, a package of fine sand, a good quality camera, a watch with a chronometer, a wet rag to put out the fire if things go wrong.

Experiment: Put the photo in the plastic bag, then the sand in the frying pan, and light the gas so that the sand heats up. Deposit a small saucepan filled with water on the sand and turn off the gas when the water reaches boiling. Remove the saucepan and throw the photo in its plastic bag on the hot sand. Take a photo of the frying pan every 10 seconds for two minutes.

You have just rendered a priceless service to science, and you now know exactly how long the Apollo 16 astronaut had to take his picture.

Shadows of Different Lengths

NASA Photograph (reference not found) (Apollo 11 mission)

Description

Armstrong and Aldrin plant the American flag on the face of the Moon.

Critical Analysis

The shadow of the astronaut holding the mast is much shorter than that of the one holding the end of the flag.

Given that it was a photograph on film taken by a Hasselblad 6x6 and not one of the LM's cameras, who took the photo?

Here is another photograph taken from the same spot:

NASA Photograph AS11-37-5545 (Apollo 11 mission)

This shot leaves no doubt about the 6x6 format of photographic equipment employed. It is difficult to conceive that NASA scientists could have provided remote control from Earth specifically to capture this moment. The utilization of a timer does not seem possible either because the height of the shot prohibits it.

Also, how was the actual shot prepared, since there was not a television camera with a remote control? Given the astronauts' busy schedules, it is difficult to imagine them making so many preparations for a photograph.

The flag seems to be a major preoccupation of the astronauts on the Moon. Can one imagine scientists spending their time planting and saluting a flag? Should we conclude that the objectives of these missions were military and political in nature?

Elements of Scientific Responses

—The fact that the lunar surface ascends behind the astronaut who is holding the mast could explain the shortening of his shadow. As the photograph was taken from above, it necessarily foreshortens the relief. A manual touch-up is possible, but it does not seem necessary. In any case, what the Sun cannot do here could not be achieved by a projector, either.

—As for triggering the shutter, the camera could have been positioned in advance within the LM, and a radio transmitter sufficed to trigger the shot on command by one of the astronauts.

Philippe Lheureux

That is an expensive way to do photography.

Excursions from the Lunar Module

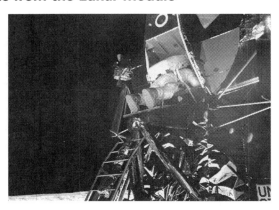

Edwin Aldrin coming out of the LM
NASA Photograph AS 11-40-5863 (Apollo 11 mission)

Neil Armstrong must have had great fun coming down first with his camera.

NASA Photograph AS11- 40-5868 (Apollo 11 mission)

NASA Photograph AS11- 40-5869 (Apollo 11 mission)

Description

This series of three photographs shows astronaut Edwin Aldrin leaving the LM.

Critical Analysis

Concerning the lighting of the scene: According to data from NASA, the Apollo 11 astronauts had neither a flash nor a reflector to fill in the parts in shadow. The Earth is almost at the zenith and is half full.

NASA Photograph AS11-40-5924 (Apollo 11 mission)

The landing zone was on a plain, and so there was no hill behind the LM to reflect the sunlight. One of the big problems of photography without a flash or a reflector is taking contrejour shots, a headache for all beginners and a disappointment to most amateurs. The exposure times are not the same for the parts that are lit and the parts in shadow. An unlit object in contre-jour will remain dark. And, if the photograph adjusts his or her camera so that the object will be correctly lit, chances are it is the background that will be overexposed and too light.

NASA Photograph AS11-40-5947 (Apollo 11 mission)

NASA Photo AS11-40-5947 leaves no doubt on this subject. It clearly shows that the shadowy areas have not been filled in on some photos. Look at the section of the LM behind the astronaut. It is completely black. That is why it is astonishing to find, in the previous photographs, that all the parts situated in the LM's shadow are visible.

And there is another surprising aberration: an unknown light source coming from the ground behind the astronaut and projecting a shadow in the reverse direction to that caused by the Sun. The manifestation of this light source can be readily observed by comparing point by point the three photographs according to this observation guide:

- The underfaces of the ladder steps and supports (the shadowed part is situated on the upper sides)
- The shadow of the bars projected onto the gold foil and the reflections in the foil
- The "United States" sign is perfectly visible (Photo AS11-40-5863).
- The reflection in the heels of the astronaut's boots (Photo AS11-40-5869) and the shadow projected over his breathing apparatus (Photo AS11-40-5868).
- The gas exhaust nozzles in the upper left are lit from below (Photo AS11-40-5863). One can even make out a shadow in the opposite direction to the solar shadow. Look closely at the shadow of the higher nozzle and compare it to those of the craters

This poses an unanswerable question: where does a light source powerful enough to fill in the contre-jour and create shadows opposite the Sun's originate? It cannot be the reflection of sunlight from the lunar surface because that surface is flat. Nor can it be from the spacesuit of the astronaut taking the photo because he is located to one side and is too small. The best hypothesis to explain the presence of this luminous source is that the photo was actually taken on Earth, with the help of all the lighting needed to obtain such professional-looking photographs.

Concerning the temperature: From my military service at Bitche, Mosel, an area in eastern France close to the German border, I can remember the winter parades when the temperature dropped to −7 degrees F. I wore two pairs of gloves, one on top of the other, and even so, after half an hour, the sensation of cold was so intense I could barely brush the metal of my gun with my gloves.

When this photo was taken, the handrails and the ladder steps are metallic and in the shade. Their temperature must be nearly −240 degrees F. Since the astronauts' gloves are the only parts of their spacesuits that are unheated, I really wonder how they managed to keep their fingers from freezing.

A question of logic: Why did Aldrin take care to close the hatch of the LM after he had come out? Ask yourself what you would do in such a situation. I suspect you would leave the hatch open in order not to stay out or to be able to retreat quickly in case of a de-pressurization problem. Does NASA procedure really call for closing the hatch, and, if so, why? The LM lacks an airlock, and so closing the hatch creates a vacuum inside. Why then, close it when there is no other life on the Moon?

In short, given that the astronauts had to exit backwards from the landing craft, closing the hatch really demanded a lot of unnecessary effort. This could be demonstrated by repeating the maneuver on Earth with the camera in a waist-high position or held in one hand.

Another commonsense question is why NASA did not anticipate the need for an extension ladder, with one part fixed, to reach the lunar surface. The last step of the ladder in this photo is situated over a yard from the surface, and the ladder is slanted. Thus, the ascent and descent could only be accomplished by a great leap forward—a leap for man, not for humanity— and the astronaut could not even see his feet. Any lunar explorer with an ounce of sense would have tried to climb back up before calling his partner to come down. And to make matters worse, the ladder's fastenings are designed in a way to obstruct certain rungs. It is surprising to see this kind of design mistake after thousands of hours of study.

Even more troubling, a photo from the Apollo 16 mission shows that the last rung of the ladder is still at least three ft. from the surface. NASA explained that, at the time of the first mission, they had expected the LM to sink more deeply into the lunar dust which had led to this "prudence" in the ladder size— which was surprising in itself. But why didn't NASA rectify the error in the following missions?

NASA Photograph AS16-113-18342 (Apollo 16 mission)

Note carefully how the shadows of the astronaut, the stones, and the footprints diverge compared to that of the LM. It is distressing. To reproduce the same effect on Earth would require a light source extremely close to the LM. The logical conclusion is that the sun—or the light source—was no more than 15 ft. behind the Lunar Module.

NASA Photograph AS12-46-6729 (Apollo 12 mission)

Lastly, here is a photo of the Apollo 12 mission which includes almost all of the anomalies mentioned above: the disturbingly short ladder, contre-jour shots with a light surface other than from the sun, and divergent shadows. It is all here.

One is led to believe that the crater beneath the LM was added to offer a more realistic touch, but a telling detail is that the surface is blackened, except in that one place. Together, this really leaves room for doubt about the lunar origins of the photographs that were released to the press.

Are the elements of scientific responses that we have insisted upon adding enough to extinguish all doubt? Here are a few:

— The surrounding luminosity was sufficient to fill in the contre-jour.

— The impression of reverse shadows is simply provoked by the black sky with the bright, solar reflection on the rungs.

— The short ladder was designed either to avoid getting in the way of astronauts' feet, or because NASA thought the LM's landing pads would sink deeper into the lunar dust, or so the pads would retract during touchdown on the Moon to act as shock absorbers.

Incoherence in the Shadows

NASA Photograph AS17-140-21388 (Apollo 17 mission)

Description

Here is an astronaut standing next to the Moon buggy. Given the presence of the American flag, this photo was probably taken close to the LM. The background is mountainous.

Critical Analysis

Given the low sun that is lighting the astronaut, the hills in the background should have a projected shadow. The surface in the foreground seems visibly darker than in the area behind it and the hills, and even in places where the astronauts have not walked. The vehicle's shadow seems proportionately shorter than that of the astronaut, while the flag's shadow seems to diverge from it. There is a dividing line running under the flag and the lunar vehicle's antenna.

It is also astonishing to notice little crosshairs for framing, like those one sees in viewfinders, appear on the astronauts' photos. Normally, on this kind of reflex camera, the cross hairs are etched on the viewfinder's glass and are not imprinted on the photo. Assuming that they are in the camera's objective lens, what purpose is served by imprinting the crosshairs on the negative? In topography, such crosses could improve the evaluation of distances, but the nature of the lunar photos are not suitable for such work.

Elements of Scientific Responses

—Let us return to the television program, *Nulle part ailleurs*[21] airing on February 22, 2000 on the Canal + Channel and the counter investigation carried out by André Brahic who commented on the same photo. Here are his words:

André Brahic—

One sees very well that the slopes here are sufficiently gentle and the Sun is sufficiently high for there to be no shadows. It has to be sufficiently low to produce a shadow.

And what we are missing in the photo in question is the three-dimensional space that has been projected onto a two-dimensional plane. To do things seriously we'd re-examine the landscape and the topography. We have the Sun's position, we do the geometry, and we'll see that there is nothing extraordinary in it. What would be astonishing would be to see a shadow of the mountain like that and another like that. (His hands make two perpendicular shadows).

And I would even say, if one believes that this photo was taken in the studio, that would have been a little naive to make so serious a mistake, they would have done a little bit better job. That shows that the photo is real; there is no problem.

Philippe Lheureux

As it happens, I am glad he said that because the flag's shadow seems perpendicular to that of the astronaut. The perpendicular shadow could be an illusion due to the presence of a crater.

Indeed, the existence of a depression could extend the astronaut's shadow. And, if the astronaut's shadow is lengthened by a depression in the ground, the sun is high enough that the mountain slopes should not cast shadows. In fact, except for the contre-jours that have been filled in well, there is not much to say about the remaining shadows. This proves that certain anomalies can be explained rationally and that one should not "cry wolf" too soon.

Challenging the authenticity of the shadows is thus a bad strategy for attacking the Moon photos. What more irrefutable proof could the astronauts give of their real presence on the Moon?

I would have liked to see them throw a boomerang, run with a miniature windmill, open a container of water beside a vacuum and film the response, or throw the lunar dust as far as possible with a shovel. In other words, do something that requires a vacuum and reduced gravity.

There was indeed an experiment with a feather and a hammer dropped at the same time, but this is too easy to falsify and leads to such questions as to how the feather withstood the change in pressure and the lunar climatic conditions (+270° F in the sun, and −240° F in the shade). While some people see a black sky and say, "such a sky could only be found on the Moon," it is easy to repaint the sky directly on the negative. The photo can be taken on Earth with a set under a beautiful blue sky and then repainted in black on the negative. It would be interesting to have the original negatives analyzed by an independent laboratory to confirm whether or not they were touched up.

Another way to find out would be to determine if there are any photos identical to those published that are under- or overexposed. Such photos would indicate the use of bracketing.

At the beginning of this book, the technique known as "bracketing," a technique of exposure, was mentioned.

Bracketing consists of taking several photographs of the same scene with different exposures. It is impossible that the bracketing technique was not used on the Moon, since there was no room for error. In this case, if there are no other identical photos, we can be sure we are in the presence of fakes.

Detail of an LM Landing Pad

NASA Photograph AS11-40-5917 (Apollo 11 mission)

Description

Detail of an LM's landing pad resting on the lunar surface.

Critical Analysis

Here we find ourselves back during the Apollo 11 mission, just as an LM is about to set down for the first time on the lunar surface. It is a brief reminder of the conditions on the Moon during the landing. According to the account at the time, the pilot had to overshoot the landing to avoid a crater field and almost ran out of fuel before he decided to land. The red lights of the computer were blinking because it was completely overwhelmed by the enormous amount of data to be registered during a lunar landing. The pilot went to manual control in order to remedy the situation. In approaching the ground, the engine raised so much dust that the pilot said he could no longer see the lunar surface.

Given that the LM was steered manually, it is difficult to imagine that its weight and the terrain's topography allowed all four of the LM's landing pads to touch down on the surface at exactly the same time—and in a gentle fashion. It is more likely that one pad touched the ground before the three others and that, under the LM's weight, the pads scraped the lunar dust slightly. It is even probable that the LM's pads must have spread out slightly after the shock before settling into their original position.

However, the photograph of the Apollo 11 landing pad does not show that it sank into the lunar dust at all. Only the bar under the pad is sunk, as if it had fallen onto clay. There is no visible sign of any lateral sliding.

This raises the question of why the pad did not leave any trace of sliding when the LM came into contact with the lunar surface. If the landing pads were articulated, it is impossible that a slight displacement did not take place upon contact.

A trench that leaves the LM's pad corresponds to the trace left by the pad's anchoring bar. Similarly, there is no sliding, and the visible swelling along this trench has a clay-like appearance.

Traces of footsteps near the bar are noticeable, as well as a triangle drawn on the ground in front of the pad. Yet, even with a footprint nearby, the lunar ground has retained its form without collapsing into the trench.

Some people will think it is normal that the LM's pad did not sink because the engine swept away the dust. But the following questions remain unanswered:

- Why did the bar sink so deeply?
- Why are there deep footprints just beside the pad?
- What created the triangular shape carved just in front of the LM's pad? If it was due to fine crevasses in the lunar surface, why is it still visible after the blast of the engine? (On Earth, that kind of ground fissuring only occurs through water evaporation, but that cannot be the case here.)
- And what should we make of the dust propelled by the LM's engine upon landing, but failed to tarnish the glitter of the gold foil surrounding the pad? Did the astronauts clean up before taking this picture?

To get to the bottom of the matter, I looked for a photograph that shows the rear of the same pad.

In the photo that follows, there are still no signs of skidding, and surprisingly, on this side, the ground is totally clear of footprints. The first thing I would have done, if I had just landed on the Moon, would be to go inspect each of the LM's landing

NASA Photograph AS11-40-5920 (Apollo 11 mission)

pads by walking around them. Instead, the experiments seem to have been carried out first. What is also very astonishing is that the ground seems to have a different texture on either side of the pad.

On the next page is a photograph showing another of the LM's landing pads. The pad farther away is the one in the preceding photograph. There is still no skid mark (due to minor sliding on landing). On this side, the lunar surface is as hard as rock. The anchoring bar is raised and has left only a faint mark on the ground.

This photograph totally contradicts the preceding one. The only common element is the fact that here, too, there is no sign of any dust on the gold foil.

NASA Photograph AS11-40-5925 (Apollo 11 mission)

Also, in this photograph, the anchoring bar is dented, as if it had received a hammering. Why? This is a mystery.

Elements of Scientific Responses

—Here is a response from Arnaud Delaunay:[22]

First of all, all this depends on whether the dust was actually LIFTED UP. And that's not at all the case, in fact. We're in a vacuum. The descent engine of the LM has chased away the first layer of dust horizontally as one can well see in the films of the lunar landings. Then, the engine was shut off once the landing contact probes touched the lunar surface, with the LM itself being some tens of inches from the ground. The pad thus touches ground when there is no longer any dust in movement.

NASA says that the triangle was made by a cable or the contact probe that was supposed to have shut down the LM's engine. That still leaves us with a lot of anomalies waiting for explanations, including:

- Different lunar surfaces from one LM pad to another
- No trace of skidding by the pads upon landing
- No trace of the blast from the engine
- A triangle made of fine crevasses that appear after the engine has stopped.

Projectors

NASA Photograph AS11-40-5872 (Apollo 11 mission)

Description

Here is Edwin Aldrin setting up an experiment about solar wind. The scene is lit from the side.

Critical Analysis

Finally, NASA has made a framing error that allows us to see the sources of light at the origin of the long shadows. Is there any other explanation that would account for these two luminous sources in the lunar sky? They're surely not UFOs. Could they be reflections of sunlight in the camera lens?

To decide this, consider the position of the projected shadow that indicates that the source of lighting is ahead and slightly to the right of the astronaut. Since when does the Sun shine on the Moon like a spot lamp?

The footprints visible on the lunar surface indicate that the astronaut taking the picture was crab-walking, almost as though he wanted to stay facing the luminous source. What a strange way of moving about!

As regards the lighting conditions of the lunar surface, look at this photograph which shows a very sunny band:

NASA Photograph AS16-112-18234 (Apollo 16 mission)

I did not know there were clouds on the Moon. Why does the Sun not light up the lunar surface evenly?

Elements of Scientific Responses
—Reflections of the Sun in the camera lens and alteration of the film
—The low sun shining between the mountains

The Same Background in Two Photographs Taken by Apollo 15
Look closely at the form of the mountains that provide a background for the next two photos. They are the same. Both of these photos were taken by Apollo 15.

Photograph of the LM against a mountainous background
NASA Photograph AS15-82-11057 (Apollo 15 mission)

File 10075727.JPG	NASA Photo ID: AS15-82-11057
File Number:	10075727.jpg
Film Type:	70mm BW
Date Taken:	31/7/71
Title:	Lunar Module photographed against lunarscape during Apollo 15 EVA

Description

The LM "Falcon" is photographed against the barren lunarscape during the Apollo 15 lunar surface extravehicular activity (EVA) at the Hadley-Apennine landing site. This view is looking southeast.

The Apennine Front is in the left background; Hadley Delta is in the right background. The object next to the flag is the Solar Wind Composition experiment. Last Crater is to the right of the LM. Note the boot prints and tracks of the Lunar Roving Vehicle. The light spherical object at the top is a reflection in the lens of the camera.

Subject terms: Apollo 15 FlightApollo Project
Craters
Extravehicular Activity
Footprints
Lunar Module
Lunar Surface
Lunar Topography
Space-borne Experiments

Recent crater against mountainous background
NASA Photograph AS15-82-11082 (Apollo 15 mission)

File 10075728.JPG	NASA Photo ID: AS15-82-11082
File Number:	10075728.jpg
Film Type:	70mm
Date Taken:	7/31/71
Title:	View of portion of "relatively fresh" crater as photographed by Apollo 15

Description

This is a close-up view of a portion of a "relatively fresh" crater, looking southeast, as photographed during the Apollo 15 lunar surface extravehicular activity at the Hadley-Apennine landing site. The Apennine Front is in the left background and Hadley Delta is in the right background.

This is a recent crater. The crater floor is much darker than the ground outside. The crater is fairly large in size since the astronaut was able to climb down into it.

Subject terms:	Apollo 15 Flight
	Apollo Project Craters
	Extravehicular Activity
	Footprints
	Lunar Surface
	Lunar Topography

Critical Analysis

The same background is found in two different photos taken during the same mission. Is this a joke? If not, then where is the LM in the second photo?

It is in front of the crater, of course. But why do we not see the crater in the photo of the LM—especially a crater of this size and shade?

I have created a montage of both photos by superimposing the two mountains, and the results speak for themselves.

NASA panoramic montage
NASA Photograph S71-43943 (Apollo 15 mission)

This is a montage comparing the two photos
NASA Photos AS15-82-11057 and AS15-82-11082
(Apollo 15 mission).

This panorama covers 360 degrees, but the crater still does not appear. And if one adds the photo AS15-88-11863 below, the mountains match up perfectly, but the two foregrounds do not.[23] You can also see the panorama put together by NASA (Photograph S71-43943) available on the Apollo 15 mission Web site. No trace of the recent crater is visible in the photo above.

David Scott saluting the American flag
NASA Photograph AS15-88-11863 (Apollo 15 mission)

File 10075741.JPG   NASA Photo ID: AS15-88-11863
File Number: 10075741.jpg
Film Type: 70mm   Date Taken: 1/8/71
Title: Astronaut David gives salute beside
                           U.S. flag during EVA

Description

This photograph was taken by the pilot Astronaut James B. Irwin, Lunar Module. In it, Astronaut David R. Scott, Commander, gives a military salute while standing beside the deployed U.S. flag during the Apollo 15 lunar surface extravehicular activity (EVA) at the Hadley-Apennine landing site. The flag was deployed toward the end of EVA-2. The Lunar Module "Falcon" is partially visible on the right. Hadley Delta rises approximately 4,000 mi. (about 13,124 ft.) in the background above the plain. The base of the mountain is approximately five km. (about three mi.) away.

The result is astonishing. The backgrounds match perfectly, but the foregrounds completely contradict each other.

Subject terms: Activity
                        Apollo 15 Flight
                        Apollo Project
                        Astronauts Ceremonies
                        Flags
                        Lunar Landing Sites
                        Lunar Module
                        Lunar Surface

The final blow comes from the aerial view of the landing site for the Apollo 15 mission. A comparison of the aerial view with the 360-degree panorama is baffling because nothing matches up. Since the mountains are about five km. from the LM, where is the horizon line on the preceding photos?

Assembly of the three photos

How and why do the official photos NASA released to the press contain such aberrations?

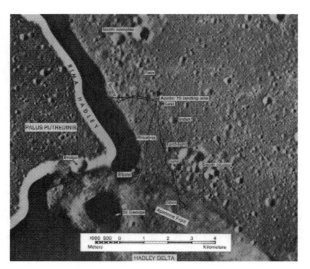

NASA Photograph showing the position of the Apollo 15 landing site

Elements of Scientific Responses

—Here is an answer from Sylvain Dionne, a Web visitor:

I just spent a whole day on your site and NASA's. At the beginning, I had doubts because your arguments were so pertinent. Nevertheless, I don't come to the same conclusions as you do.

The most convincing item on your site is the study of the two photos, AS15-82-11057 and AS15-82-11082, claiming that the same backdrop was used for two different subjects. I found these photos on NASA's site and the text that accompanies them indicates that the mountains we see are the SAME. So how does one explain that the foregrounds have changed?

That's simple, but you need to know some photography. I have been practicing this as a hobby since I was 15.

The foregrounds change because the focal length of the camera lens changes. The angle of vision of a photo depends on the power of the lens, a wide-angle lens is going to cover more terrain than a telescopic lens. For the photo in which we see the LM, the photographer used a telescopic lens and was placed well behind the LM. As far as the other photo is concerned, it was taken beside the LM with a wide-angle. That's why one sees the ground dug up and why the mountains are the same. I made a sketch to visualize this phenomenon better.

Philippe Lheureux

There is indeed a crater to the right of the LM, but its shade does not correspond at all with that in photo AS15-83-11082 (see NASA's panorama).

You need to know that a photo taken with a wide-angle lens has little chance of being superimposed exactly with one taken by a telescopic lens. The wide-angle has a tendency to shrink subjects in the background.

But then again, the panorama composed by the camera situated near the LM shows the same match of photographs.[24]

A LM From the Apollo 17 Mission Disappears from Photos?

Here is a photograph of the LM and the flag from the Apollo 17 mission:

Apollo 17 Lunar Module against a mountainous background
NASA Photograph AS17-134-20508 (Apollo 17 mission)

. . . and an image taken behind the LM of the Apollo 17 mission. One readily notes the same tracks on the ground as in the preceding photograph.

The same mountain taken just behind the LM
NASA Photograph AS17-149-21374 (Apollo 17 mission)

Here is the Moon buggy parked at station 8:

And now . . . the LM vanishes.
NASA Photograph AS17-146-22367 (Apollo 17 mission)

Critical Analysis

There is no trace of the LM, although the machine should remain visible, given its position in the two preceding pages. As for the tracks on the ground, they have simply disappeared. Landmarks, nevertheless, persist, such as the position of certain stones between points No. 1 and 2 that were visible in the last photo.

Here are Cernan and the Moon buggy at station 6:

Is NASA a better magician than David Copperfield? NASA Photograph AS17-141-21598 (Apollo 17 mission)

Critical Analysis

There is still no trace of the LM. It seems to have vanished into thin air. But this photograph covers the entire field to the left of point No. 1.

Here are Schmitt and the Moon buggy:

The LM has well and truly disappeared NASA Photograph AS17-146-22296 (Apollo 17 mission)

Critical Analysis

Still no trace of the LM, even to the right of point No. 2

Elements of Scientific Responses

—It is probably from effects of the telephoto lens, squashing the perspective. The LM is located somewhere between the photos.

Concerning the Samples

When mere photographs do not suffice, something concrete is required. So, let us see if the concrete evidence withstands critical analysis any better than the photos.

The most widespread argument used to prove the Americans did land on the Moon is that they brought back samples. According to books and articles, the samples are basalt of the same isotopic composition as on Earth.

Here are some impressions of the samples that were brought back.

An initial disappointment: Why was not even a single element different from what exists on Earth found? Some new metal that might have served as proof? Certain elements like iron, titanium, and magnesium are present in different concentrations, but there is nothing that could not be fabricated in a laboratory using terrestrial rocks.

Given the number of meteorites that arrive on the lunar surface, it seems astonishing that the astronauts did not bring back samples with interesting elements. Also, there is debris from meteorites on Earth.

And here is a second disappointment: Why were the Russians not given the right to analyze the samples? If they could do so, why did they return in 1976 to look for more? Is the Russians' analysis compatible with that of the Americans'? If the Americans had found something really interesting on the Moon, it is easy to understand why they would not have been in a hurry to divulge it to other countries. Remember the gold rush.

The 1999 launch of the American probe Lunar Prospector, dedicated to administering surveys, does prove that Americans are very interested in the nature of the lunar surface. Since it is not usual to spend millions of dollars on basalt, there is probably something much more interesting up there.

Harrison Schmitt collecting samples
NASA Photograph AS17-134-20425 (Apollo 17 mission)

Dig or take pictures? He had to make a choice. It almost seems like the photos released to the press were a catalog of problems to avoid during a lunar mission.

Concerning the laser reflectors

Here is the basic principle behind the use of these devices. A laser beam emitted by a terrestrial station should reflect off a mirror placed on the Moon and return to a terrestrial receiver. Knowing the speed of light, one can deduce with precision the distance between the Earth and the Moon. Thus, with the help of these laser reflectors, scientists have been able to calculate that the Moon is moving away from the Earth at a rate of two to three in. per year.[25]

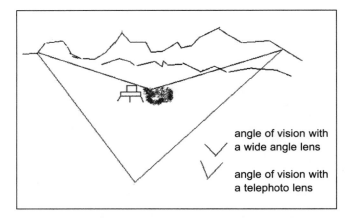

angle of vision with
a wide angle lens

angle of vision with
a telephoto lens

Rationalists will be quick to say: "If the laser beams emitted from the Earth have been reflected back to us, it is because mirrors were placed on the Moon by the American astronauts." However, that is not certain because it is also possible a robot left the mirrors on the Moon, and no humans were present at all.

For example, let us imagine a device looking like the lower portion of an LM covered by a mirror. The piloting could have been done from the capsule that remained in orbit. It simply would have required cameras to retransmit what could be seen from the descent module.

That said, my aim is not to demonstrate that the Americans did not set foot on the Moon but to suggest that the photographs released to the press are a form of disinformation designed to protect their discoveries.

On the Web site devoted to the French Moon Laser Telemetry Station,[26] the FAQ section contains the following information:

The two French reflectors placed by Soviet automatic probes are composed of 14 cube corners of about 106 mm.

per side; the American reflectors left by Apollo XI and XIV are both composed of a hundred cub corners but are smaller (38.2 mm.), while the Apollo XV reflector has about 400 cube corners and is the biggest.

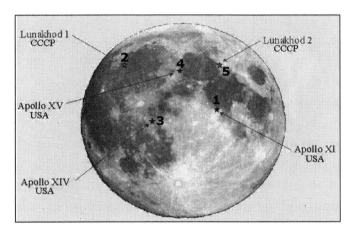

Positions of laser reflectors by order of their placement on the Moon

This proves that placing a mirror on the Moon can be carried out without a human presence since the Russians did so in 1970 by remote control from Earth. However, it does not answer these questions:

- Why was a fifth reflector deposited after the Apollo 15 mission?
- Were the Russians unable to use the American reflectors? Since a mirror does not care at all about the nationality of the laser beam it reflects, this seems unlikely.
- Why, then, conduct costly parallel missions to duplicate the same result as the Americans?

Alternative Conclusions

What is astonishing in carrying out this critical analysis of the NASA photographs is that a good number of readers all agree on one point: anomalies exist in the photographs released to the press.

That the man on the street, more preoccupied by the spectacle and the artistic aspect of the photographs, has not expressed doubts is understandable. In contrast, it is hard to understand why no one else, especially scientists asked questions. Are they afraid of ridicule? Have they been silenced by politicians? Were they, too, hypnotized by the grandeur of the event?

And what about the Soviets? Why did they not challenge the authenticity of the photos?

More than 30 years after the fact, I decided to take an anonymous poll to capture the opinions of readers of this book by nationality. It can be found at *http://lheureux.free.fr/sondage.html*

This is an opportunity for you to voice your opinion. After reading this book, it is up to you to choose and vote for the conclusion that seems most realistic to you. Vote first (to avoid being unduly influenced) and then look at the results of the poll to see whether or not your opinion differs from those of other readers.[27]

Here are a few hypotheses, listed in order of increasing paranoia:

Hypothesis No. 1: The photographs are real.

NASA undoubtedly sent men to the Moon. The photographs released are indeed the real photographs of the event and have not been retouched. The pseudo-anomalies only exist in the minds of people incapable of adapting to progress or possessing intellectual faculties that are below average.

The aim of NASA is to further science. That is why the photographs and samples were disseminated throughout the world. The missions were then abandoned because they were too costly.

Any disagreement with the above is only revisionism or disinformation.

Hypothesis No. 2: The photos were touched up for artistic or "public relations" purposes.

The photographs released are indeed the real photographs of this event, but some of them have been retouched in the interests of publicity (the signs "United States" and "NASA" should be readable, etc.) and were cropped or colorized for artistic reasons. But nothing has been altered that really calls into question the status of this marvelous event.

The anomalies that are visible are due purely to the fact that the brain is confused by the fact that there are differences between the ways the laws of physics (as they affect lighting, vacuum, gravity, the horizon) operate on the Moon as opposed to on Earth.

Hypothesis No. 3: The photographs were spoiled in the first mission and had to be redone in the studio.

Given the lunar climatic conditions described above, the Apollo 11 astronauts ruined all or some of their photographs from the mission on the lunar surface. Due to the political stakes, the officials at NASA made the decision to publish photographs taken during training in order to conceal this mistake.

Later, in order to prevent this deception from being unmasked, they did the same thing with photographs from other missions. The real photos from those missions have not been published for that reason.

Hypothesis No. 4: The photographs of all of the missions were ruined.

Because the lunar climatic conditions proved too difficult, it was impossible to take photographs on the Moon correctly. To remedy the situation, NASA officials issued photographs taken during training and continued to do so throughout the remaining missions. This explains certain errors visible in the photographs.

Hypothesis No. 5: NASA deliberately kept the real photographs for themselves.

The Apollo missions were military missions cleverly camouflaged as scientific ones. In order to protect discoveries with potential military applications (e.g. the installation of nuclear missile bases on the Moon), NASA suppressed the real photographs and published others that were expurgated of any content that was scientifically or militarily useful.

Americans are not philanthropists and did not spend millions of dollars just to transmit the real photographs for free to humanity. The photographs released are probably disinformation aimed to protect their scientific discoveries and satisfy the American taxpayer. By publishing fake photographs, they killed two birds with one stone.

Hypothesis No. 6: NASA could not reveal to the world what the astronauts saw up there.

"There is a Santa Claus." Everyone remembers those words Frank Borman (Apollo 8 mission) uttered when radio contact was reestablished after his spacecraft came out from the hidden face of the Moon.

The Apollo missions were military missions intended to verify what astronomers and UFO experts had already surmised from their observations:

- The Moon is colonized by extraterrestrials, and many of its craters are linked to mining operations.

- The real purpose of the missions was to collect information about UFO bases. In order to obtain funding without revealing this goal, studio shots were taken based on real photographs from the Moon. These pictures have no scientific value but are there to reassure taxpayers.

- That is why the Russians did not contest the authenticity of the photographs. They, too, knew that there were ET bases on the Moon, and they collaborated with the Americans.

- Any attempt to conquer the Moon was abandoned because it was already occupied. Landing on it would risk arousing the hostility of the ETs.

- The military probes specialized in lunar cartography, Clementine, launched in 1994 and, more recently, the Lunar Prospector satellite, showed that Americans are trying to understand why the Moon interests the ETs.

- The *Cometa Report* released in France in July, 1999 makes official the existence of UFOs in France and indicates that politicians in other countries are also aware of this and are slowly beginning to prepare public opinion.[28]

Hypothesis No. 7: No one landed on the Moon.

NASA has never sent man to the Moon. They just flew around it. All of the photographs were produced in a secret base situated in the volcanic mountains of Arizona where an area of the Moon was reconstituted for the occasion. Later, all NASA needed to do was retouch the blue sky as black to give the illusion that the photographs taken on the Moon. The Moon rocks were all brought back by unmanned probes.

The purpose was political propaganda and to drain funds into armament in order to win the psychological war with the Russians. Today, no country is capable of going there, not even the Americans.

Hypothesis No. 8: Other
As Fox Mulder would say, "the truth is out there."

With eight possibilities, you probably wonder which ones I like the best. André Brahic asked me not to conclude too hastily, and I have kept my word. However, I tend to favor two, five, six, and seven.

I like No. 2 because to err is human. Also, because it is here that several things I noticed finally found a rational explanation. In fact, it is much easier to raise questions than to find the answers. Anybody can ask what is the distance between Earth and Jupiter, but few are really capable of calculating it. And above all, not knowing the answer does not call into question the fact that there exists a distance between Earth and Jupiter. It is probably the same in the case of the conquest of the Moon. At least I hope so.

I chose No. 5 because it fits well with the paranoid mentality of the military. Certain people will rush to add with a touch of humor that, as far as paranoids go, I can hold my own.

No. 6 allows us the right to dream. What good would the Moon be if it did not have an extraterrestrial base upon it? This is what we will see in Chapter Three. Those who think I have spoiled their dream by denigrating the Apollo missions will have the opportunity to dream again, I promise.

No. 7 acknowledges the right to doubt. In all my research, I never really found an article of evidence that supports the reality of the missions. The LM landing pad showed no sign of any engine blast, the spacesuits are not inflated, the depth of the footprints on the surface is wrong, the shadows or backgrounds don't "fit," the aperture of the camera lens is incompatible with capturing dim lights, there is no bracketing, the LM takes off without any flames, there is no airlock, etc.

I feel it coming over me again. Is it serious, doctor?

Internet Links on the Same Subjects

Sites on electronic levitation
In English:

http://www.space.com/scienceastronomy/top_10_weird_list-7.html

Sites criticizing the Apollo missions
In English

Apollo Moon Mission Anomalies and Inconsistencies (David Wozney)—
http://internet.ocii.com/~dpwozney/apollo1.htm

I found this Web site after having written my book and noticed that David Wolsey had picked up on the same anomalies. He discusses research that takes up in detail several points raised in this book and brings some scientific calculations to address them.

The Dark Side of the Moon Landings—
http://www.fortean-times.com/articles/094_ moon.shtml

This site includes an article outlining the observations of photographer David Percy.

Faked Moon Landings (Kevin Overstreet)—
http://batesmotel.8m.com/

In French:
Secret Links (Bernard Heliord)—
http://www.chez.com/ahb/secret.html
Everything about plots, UFOs, etc.can be found here.

Sites answering critics of the missions
In English:

Fox TV and the Apollo Moon Hoax—
http://www.badastroNomy.com/bad/tv/foxapollo.html
This provides a detailed rebuttal of the Fox television program,
"Conspiracy Theory: Did We Land on the Moon?"

NASA's Moon Hoax—
http://www.redzero.demon.co.uk/moonhoax/

Apollo Hoax—
http://www.apollo-hoax.co.uk

Moon Landing Hoax—
http://moonhoax1.tripod.com/MoonHoax/id1.html

In French:

The Moon Landings Were Not Faked (Arnaud Delaunay)—
http://perso.clubinternet.fr/arnaudel/Payekhali/Dossiers/Anti-TMLWF.htm

A Critical Analysis of the Web Site, A Step Too Far on the
Moon (Arnaud Delaunay)—
http://perso.clubinternet.fr/arnaudel/Payekhali/Dossiers/Contre-analyse-intro.html

A superb piece of work demolishing my arguments, not to be missed for any reason.

Response from the Physics Laboratory—
http://franck.germain.free.fr/nasa/apollo.htm

Apollo X-Files. Response to a Revisionist—
http://chabin.laurent.free.fr/nasa/nasa_hoax.htm

The Lunar Missions—
http://membres.lycos.fr/jcboulay/astro/sommaire/astronautique/missions_lunaires/missions.htm

This is a link to an interesting chronology of the Moon race.

Moon Landings

🌙

Chapter Two

UFOs

Any revelation of a secret is the fault of he who confided it.
—*La Bruyère*

Is the Moon a base for UFOs? If they really exist, it is possible. Here are some pages that tend to show that the Moon is probably more "alive" than is usually believed.

Two Minutes of Radio "Silence"

An unverified report available via Internet[29] asserts that Neil Armstrong and Edwin Aldrin saw UFOs shortly after landing on the Moon.

One of the astronauts said he saw a light in a crater. When Houston asked him for details, televised communication was cut off. But an amateur radio operator, listening to the frequency, said he recorded the following dialogue:

Armstrong/Aldrin: *Those are giant things. No, No, No, this is not an optical illusion. No one is going to believe this.*

Houston (Christopher Craft): *What . . . what . . . what? What the hell is happening? What's wrong with you?*

Armstrong/Aldrin: *They're here under the surface.*

Houston: *What's there? [muffled noise] Emission interrupted: interference control calling Apollo 11.*

Armstrong/Aldrin: *We saw some visitors. They were here for a while, observing the instruments.*

Houston: *Repeat your last information.*

Armstrong/Aldrin: *I say that there were other spaceships. They're lined up in the other side of the crater.*

Houston: *Repeat . . . repeat.*

Armstrong/Aldrin: *Let us sound this orbital . . . in 625 to five . . . automatic relay connected . . . My hands are shaking so badly I can't do anything. Film it? God, if these damned cameras have picked up anything, what then?*

Houston: *Have you picked up anything?*

Armstrong/Aldrin: *I didn't have any film at hand. Three shots of the saucers, or whatever they were ruining the film.*

Houston: *Control, control here. Are you on your way? What is the uproar with the UFOs over?*

Armstrong/Aldrin: *They've landed there. There they are and they're watching us.*

Houston: *The mirrors, the mirrors, have you set them up?*

Armstrong/Aldrin: *Yes, they're in the right place. But whoever made those spaceships surely can come tomorrow and remove them. Over and out.*

Critical Analysis

The phrase, "Let us sound this orbital . . . in 625 to five . . . automatic relay connected . . ." implies the astronauts were flying over the Moon at the moment they saw the UFOs. They were not on the surface. In any case, I have trouble imagining

Armstrong and Aldrin calmly proceeding with their experiments on the Moon after having witnessed the presence of UFOs.

As to the mirrors, which were probably the laser reflectors intended to measure the distance from the Earth to the Moon, what prevented them from being deposited from a distance by remote control?

A Close Encounter of the Third Kind in the Bible?

Here is an excerpt from the Book of Ezekiel (Old Testament), King James version:[30]

And I looked, and, behold, a whirlwind came out of the north, a great cloud, and a fire enfolding itself, and a brightness was about it, and out of the midst thereof as the color of amber, out of the midst of the fire.

Also out of the midst thereof came the likeness of four living creatures. And this was their appearance; they had the likeness of a man. And every one had four faces, and every one had four wings. And their feet were straight feet; and the sole of their feet was like the sole of a calf's foot; and they sparkled like the color of burnished brass. And they had the hands of a man under their wings on their four sides; and each of the four had their faces and their wings.

Does this not remind you of anything?

Their wings were joined one to another; they turned not when they went; they went every one straight forward. As for the likeness of their faces, they four had the face of a man, and the face of a lion, on the right side: and they four had the face of an ox on the left side; they four also had the face of an eagle. Thus were their faces: and their wings were stretched upward; two wings of every one were joined one to another, and two covered their bodies. And they went every one straight forward: whither the spirit was to go, they went; and they turned not when they went. As for the likeness of the living creatures, their appearance was like burning coals of fire, and like the appearance of lamps: it went up and down among the living creatures; and the fire was bright, and out of the fire went forth lightning. And the living creatures ran and returned as the appearance of a flash of lightning.

Now as I beheld the living creatures, behold one wheel upon the earth by the living creatures, with his four faces. The appearance of the wheels and their work was like unto the color of a beryl: and they four had one likeness: and their appearance and their work was as it were a wheel in the middle of a wheel. *When they went, they went upon their four sides: and they turned not when they went.* As for their rings, they were so high that they were dreadful; and their rings were full of eyes round about them four. *And when the living creatures went, the wheels went by them:* and when the living creatures were lifted up from the earth, the wheels were lifted up. *Whithersoever the spirit was to go, they went, thither was their spirit to go;* and the wheels were lifted up over against them: for the spirit of the living creature was in *the wheels. <u>When those went, these went; and when those stood, these stood</u>; and when those were lifted up from the earth, the wheels were lifted up over against them: for the spirit of the living creature was in the wheels.*

And the likeness of the firmament upon the heads of the living creature was as the color of the terrible crystal, stretched forth over their heads above. And under the firmament were their wings straight, the one toward the other: <u>every one had two, which covered on this side, and every one had two, which covered on that side, their bodies</u>.

A likeness of man? A firmament the color of crystal over their heads? Straight wings on their back and joined together? Straight feet like those of a calf? Strange, I have seen this before somewhere.

And when they went, I heard the noise of their wings, like the noise of great waters, as the voice of the Almighty, the voice of speech, as the noise of a host: when they stood, they let down their wings. And there was a voice from the firmament that was over their heads, when they stood, and had let down their wings.

And above the firmament that was over their heads was the likeness of a throne, as the appearance of a sapphire stone: and upon the likeness of the throne was the likeness as the appearance of a man above upon it. And I saw as the color of amber, as the appearance of fire round about within it, from the appearance of his loins even upward, and from the appearance of his loins even downward, I saw as it were the appearance of fire, and it had brightness round about. As the appearance of the bow that is in the cloud in the day of rain, so was the appearance of the brightness round about.

This was the appearance of the likeness of the glory of the LORD. And when I saw it, I fell upon my face, and I heard a voice of one that spoke.

Conclusion

This close encounter of the third kind, right in the middle of the Bible, seems astonishing to me. Imagine the flying saucers with their windows (their height and span are frightening and the circumference of the four wheels are filled with eyes). As for the firmament of crystal, what is a firmament if not a hemisphere, and what could it represent if not the visor of an astronaut's helmet?

This description from Ezekiel lends credence to the possibility of a contact with a highly evolved civilization of terrestrial or extraterrestrial origin. Could this civilization be the source of the artificial craters visible on the Moon? You will find out when you read Chapter Three. There is also a book by Jean Sendy on the subject: *La Lune, Clé de la Bible.*[31]

If a link with the theses developed by the Raelians seems to exist, I have nothing to do with that sect whose ideas I oppose. This interpretation is just here to establish the transition between the photographs of the lunar landings and the theory of artificial craters. It was interesting to notice how the photo of Aldrin resembles Ezekiel's description.

Orion and Apollo

Here is the emblem of the Apollo missions as can be seen on NASA's Web site:

It shows a rocket leaving Earth, passing in front of the constellation Orion, and landing on the Moon, whose shadows resemble a human face looking at Orion. The bar of the "A" is created by the Betelgeuse, Rigel, and Bellatrix, the three stars of the shield and the trace of the rocket's trajectory.

Are we in mythology or the 20th century here? Why has the Moon race been transformed into thumbing one's nose at Orion's sinister forces? Were the Russians forgotten in favor of a threat from the stars?[32]

In mythology, Orion was a giant hunter. He was killed by Artemis whom he had offended. After his death, Artemis transformed him into a constellation at the same time that his dog Sirius became a star. A giant—perhaps like those in the Bible?

Genesis, Chapter 6: Verse 2—
The sons of God saw that the daughters of men were fair; and they took wives all of which they chose.

Verse 4—
There were giants in the earth in those days; and also after that, when the sons of God came in unto the daughters of men, and they bore children to them.

A literal interpretation of the Bible tells a story of an extraterrestrial race that was taken to be gods and who coupled with Earth women to give birth to giants. The same became mighty men which were heroes of old, men of renown.

What does the Apollo mission have to do with all this? The more I look at the emblem, the more it inspires me to say, "I see you; we know you exist," and "Don't come near the Moon, or you'll end up like Orion."

NASA really lays it on thick, and then they're astonished when some people see extraterrestrials everywhere.

The Cometa Report

Until the Cometa Report was published in July, 1999, the

only forms attributed to UFOs were lenticular-shaped clouds, stars, satellites, stealth planes, the Moon, or weather balloons seen by drunks or by people wanting to attract attention. Scientists admitted the possible existence of extraterrestrials, but their planets were much too far away for them to come visit us. Human technology was officially declared the "best in the universe." No extraterrestrial race could surpass us. In short, it was better to see nothing then to come across as a nutcase.

Judging by the report titled, *Les ovni et la défense – A quoi doit-on se preparer*[33] which was presented confidentially to the French President and Prime Minister, this is no longer the case. It has a preface from General Norlain, former director of the Institut des Hautes Etudes de Défense Nationale (serious business, then).

Those who have bought the *Cometa Report*[34] are familiar with the following:

Studies by the Centre National d'Etudes Spatiales, the French gendarmerie and the French Air Force carried out over a period of 20 years show the almost certain physical reality of totally unknown flying objects, remarkable in terms of their flight performance and silence, apparently moved by intelligent forces. The maneuvers of flying objects leave a strong impression on both civilian and military pilots, who hesitate to speak of them. The fear of seeming ridiculous, deranged, or simply credulous is the principal motive of their reticence.

A sole hypothesis accounts sufficiently for the facts in the light of existing science: that of extraterrestrial visitors.

The extraterrestrial hypothesis is by far the best scientific hypothesis. It is of course not proven in a categorical fashion, but there exist strong presumptions in its favor, and if it turns out to be correct, it has major consequences.

No, you're not dreaming. All this is down in black-and-white in the report. Worse still, it implies that the American military has kept hidden an important secret that occurred at Roswell in 1947.

Certain rationalist extremists, such as those of Zetetic[35] Circle, will say that this report is inadmissible and that those who wrote it have been manipulated by cranks. But how much weight does the opinion of professional stage magicians carry compared to the evidence of radar signatures and the testimony of Air Force pilots?

Just who were the authors of the *Cometa Report* and who should be praised for having spoken the truth? They include General Bernard Norlain (former head of the IHEDN),[36] Jean Claude Ribes (a famous astrophysicist), Professor André Lebeau (former president of the CNES),[37] Marc Merlo (French admiral) Alain Orszag (weapons engineer), General Denis Letty (French Air Force), Christian Marchal (chief mining engineer), Michel Algrin (lawyer), Pierre Bescond (weapons engineer), Denis Blanchard (national police commissioner at the French Ministry of the Interior), General Bruno Le Moine (French Air Force), Françoise Lépine (French Defense Studies Foundation), and Jean Dunglas (doctor of engineering).

Certainly, they are a far cry from the traditional fringe researchers on the subject of UFOs. Yet, who has heard the *Cometa Report* mentioned on television or radio? Have journalists received orders not to pay attention to this source of information? I would like to see them examine the NASA photos[38] (or those of the Clementine lunar probe).[39]

But getting back to the subject of UFOs, since it now seems that the "extraterrestrial" hypothesis is by far the strongest scientific hypothesis, it would seem that the Moon is a good base to observe us without taking risks.

Here is a photo taken by the Clementine satellite that seems to support this hypothesis:

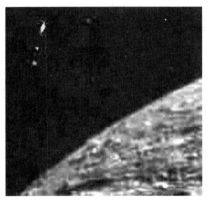

Clementine photo (NASA)

There is a white point in the upper left of the photo near the Moon. The photo is digital, so it cannot be a question of dust on the negative. Could it be a UFO? (I have trouble imagining the American military ignoring the UFO problem and limiting the Apollo missions to a "shovel, bucket, and flag" operation.)

Is the Moon Hollow?

During the Apollo 12 mission, the final scientific experiment consisted of an attempt to determine the Moon's internal structure by analyzing a shock wave. The LM, emptied of its occupants, was programmed to crash into the lunar Ocean of Storms, about 50 mi. from the seismograph left on the surface by the astronauts.

The results were astonishing. The impact caused very long waves that had a weak speed of propagation, lasting 30 minutes.[40] It seemed as if the Moon was hollow and had been made to vibrate like a bell.

No scientist really knew what to make of these results. Some UFO researchers think that the Moon is a gigantic extraterrestrial space vessel deliberately placed in orbit around the Earth in ancient times. For them, the craters are only dents in a protective shell. The hidden face of the Moon that bears a greater number of craters was the main shield during the preceding voyage. It must be admitted that this experiment provided ammunition to support their case.

Critical Analysis

We need to know whether this experiment was repeated by another mission. Were the results the same? To my way of thinking, it would have been more "scientific" to place explosives on the Moon's surface in order to measure the propagation of a shock wave since the strength and the exact position of the explosion would have been known. Apollo 12 could have left several explosive devices destined to detonate by a subsequent mission. The data from two seismographs deposited in different locations would have been correlated to give more definitive results.

Some other questions that occurred to me include:

- Could the seismograph have recorded something other than the crash of the LM?
- If, as the reader will discover in Chapter Three, certain craters have been deliberately shaped, could the vibrations that were recorded have been caused by machinery at work in a crater?

Transient Lunar Phenomena Have Never Been Studied

For most scientists, the Moon is a dead star. All volcanic activity is supposed to have ceased over a billion years ago. But despite that, many serious astronomers (both current and former) have claimed to have seen unexplained phenomena they labeled Transient Lunar Phenomena (TLPs). Under the title *The Moon is Alive,* one Web site, among many others, related observations that were collected at the beginning of the 1990's and which have been regularly repeated since man has looked at the Moon with the aid of magnifying lenses: "Glows that are probably due to dust lifted by puffs of gas have been observed on the Moon, showing that the Earth's natural satellite is not totally extinguished," revealed astronomer Audouin Dollfus, of the Paris-Meudon Observatory.

Scientists know that a period of intense volcanic and magmatic activity opened on the Moon 4.2 billion years ago, but they generally believe this activity ceased over a billion years ago. The appearance of sporadic glows on the lunar surface, inside Langrenus Crater, seems to contradict this.

Later, the author of the article said:

. . . the examination of a series of photos of the bottom of this crater taken a few years ago at intervals of a few days on average, using the Meudon telescope, have brought to light unexpected changes. Indeed, photos taken on December 29, 1992 with a new instrument, a video-polarimeter, which produces both classic pictures and images formed by polarized light, show the bottom of the crater without any anomaly. The next day, illuminations appeared, and shone both in the "normal" picture and in polarized light [. . .] These events, [professor Dollfus explained], *appeared at the center of a big crater formed by an ancient impact, which fractured and broke up the surface. In addition, this crater was formed at the periphery of a vast basin, the Sea of Fertility, which also resulted from a very big impact. The region must thus be particularly fractured and fissured, and this texture is propitious for the extrusion of gas.*

Such phenomena occur at a rate of about 30 to 35 times each year. In 1969 (the year of Apollo 11), 118 were observed.

What is happening here? Essentially, very bright flashes or white spots, appearing in or close to certain craters. But that is not all. Among the unexplained anomalies found by both professional and amateur observers, are:

- **occultations** of the relief and a temporary obscuring of features, probably linked to dust upheavals;
- **red or blue glows,** which may or may not blink.

And there are even modifications in the form of certain craters such as Messier Crater or Linné Crater.

Many TLPs were photographed and listed well before the Apollo missions. The most rational explanation for them would be that immense pockets of volcanic gas exist beneath the lunar crust which end up escaping and, in the process, raise enormous quantities of lunar dust. The sunlight striking the gas and the dust cloud gives rise to these strange phenomena visible from Earth.

Critical Analysis

Those TLPs that have been observed are perhaps signs of intelligent extraterrestrial activity in the lunar craters. It is possible that mining operations could very well produce effects analogous to those described above.

It is abnormal to discard the hypothesis of life on the Moon before having even studied it. Especially when one knows that certain craters have a polygonal form.[41]

Internet Links on the Same Subjects

Sites on the *Cometa Report*

In French:

Ovni : Quand le Cometa paraît[42]—
http://sciencefrontieres.free.fr/art/cometa.htm

Sites on TLPs

In English:

Chronological catalog of reported lunar events—
http://www.eskimo.com/~pierres/Nasa/tech01.html

The Lunascan Project (TLP) —
http://www.evansville.net/~slk/-lunascan.html

NASA Technical Report R-277:
Transient Lunar Phenomena —
http://www.mufor.org/tlp/lunar.html

Since it was a report from NASA itself, mission controllers had to account for it in selecting landing sites.

In French:
Les phénomènes transitoires lunaires[43]
http://www.astrosurf.com/sirius/ptl1.html

This is an excellent article. Look out for the Table of Transient Lunar Phenomena in the Appendix.

Chapter Three

The Artificial Craters Theory

Warning: If you lack an open mind, there is no use reading further, except perhaps for a good laugh. In any case, if you continue, you will never look at the Moon with the same eyes again.

You may recall the very first words uttered by Frank Borman (Apollo 8) upon reestablishing radio contact after the first flight over the hidden face of the Moon on Christmas, 1968: "Please be informed there is a Santa Claus." What had he seen to utter such words at that precise moment?

In 1980 in the Parisian Metro, I noticed a man sitting in front of me reading a book with a surprising title: *Somebody Else Is on the Moon* by George H. Leonard.[44] Out of curiosity, I acquired a copy. I do not know if it is still available. Here is the publisher's summary of the book's contents:

> *This book, which George Leonard succeeded in getting into print despite the opposition of American public agencies, will have the effect of a bomb going off.*
>
> *George Leonard affirms and demonstrates, based on the evidence of NASA's own official photographs, the incredible truth: the Moon is inhabited. NASA's astronauts have witnessed this with their own eyes, but they are strictly obeying orders to remain silent. "My book," says George Leonard, "is the result of a veritable police investigation and years of considerable research. I've studied and*

scrutinized thousands of NASA photographs; I've had innumerable conversations with team members working on space programs: we have to force the American government and NASA to tell the entire truth, and then, press for massive landings on the Moon.

Once they get into the details of a particularly rigorous demonstration, readers will find it difficult not to be persuaded by George Leonard's extraordinary revelations, which call into question the overly reassuring body of current scientific thinking and lead to the new formulation, in military and economic terms, of a strategy on a cosmic scale.

I thought at first that the author had "blown a fuse" mentally. It was the sort of book one might give to a friend on April Fools' Day. Extraterrestrials on the Moon? What will they think of next?

If it were true, it would have come to light long ago, and, instead of the massive landings called for by the author, caution would be the order of the day. Moreover, why would they choose the Moon when the Earth is so much more hospitable?

The hoax really seemed much too blatant. Why would such a discovery be hidden? The author must be crazy.

I suspect that you will have the same opinion about me in a very short while, and that's quite normal. It is the logical reaction of a mind conditioned to think rationally when confronted with a new idea—rejection on principle.

Are human beings afraid of the consequences of the discovery of a more evolved form of life than our own? God created man in His image. But, if extraterrestrials that are more intelligent than we exist, that threatens to call into question a good number of terrestrial beliefs.

And then, how can we accept that they are out there watching us with the same regard that we have for ants? It is more reassuring to imagine them far away than to know that they are close to home.

Nor is it common to call into question established scientific truths. Since the Apollo missions, everyone thinks that the Moon is nothing but a sort of sterile desert without an atmosphere, completely unsuited to life as we know it. That is true, but nothing would have prevented either an extraterrestrial or an ancient terrestrial civilization from sending machines there. After all, we have done that.

Personally, I am persuaded that life is not an isolated phenomenon associated solely with Earth but one that pervades the universe. The 1979 discovery of an entire submarine food chain (bacteria, worms, mussels, Octopi) living in water at temperatures close to 660 degrees F., in complete darkness, with the pressures at a depth of 7,500 ft., and in an environment rich in sulphur, hydrogen sulfide, and ammonia, has only strengthened my opinion.[45]

If life has been able to adapt to these extreme conditions, then it could have colonized other planets. This could take the form of bacteria since an octopus has been filmed on Earth living in the water in proximity to thermophilic bacteria. Since the octopus is an intelligent animal, this would seem to increase the chances of one day finding a planet where life has reached a superior state of consciousness.

It is pointless to invest in a telescope since the Moon has become accessible 24 hours a day on the Internet. In 1980, it was impossible to verify the photographs in the book, *Somebody Else is on the Moon*. Today, with Internet, the task is possible via Web sites such as those devoted to the Clementine[46] and Lunar Orbiter[47] missions. The Clementine site provides 1.8 million photographs of the lunar surface taken by a military probe in 1994.

For the purposes of this investigation, I have provided some representative photographs that will not fail to arouse your curiosity. At the very least, when confronted with such pictures, we need to ask questions and try to come up with answers to them.

Out of the 1.8 million pictures taken by Clementine, I studied about 250 before presenting this investigation to you. This should show that the anomalies are fairly frequent. Nevertheless, it may be the case that I have interpreted what I see in the pictures erroneously. It is up to you to form your own opinion.

For your information, the photographs taken by the Clementine probe and displayed in this book have a resolution of 240 ft., that is to say, a screen pixel equals approximately 240 ft. Any object whose size is less than this resolution remains invisible. It is useless to hope to spot the LM or an extraterrestrial at a landing site. Nonetheless, remember that everything visible is actually gigantic and thus could not be the result of human technology, if technology is involved.

Here, then, are the photos that pose problems for me.

The Polygonal Craters

These photographs clearly raise a question about the

existence of a form of intelligence on the Moon. To facilitate the spotting of anomalies, most have been accompanied by a drawing indicating their position.

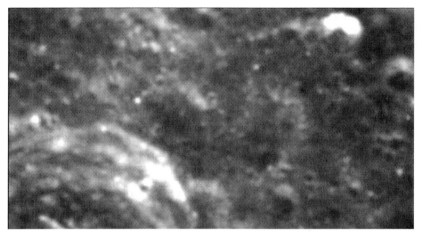

Polygonal crater (Clementine photograph, NASA)

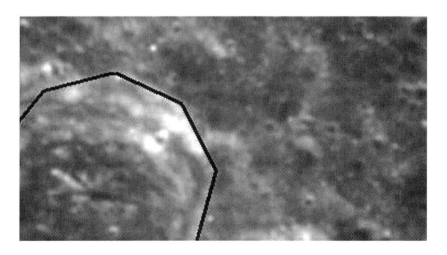

Anomalies highlighted

On the left of the photograph, the polygonal shape of the isolated crater stands out. The Moon harbors a lot of polygonal craters, something I had known nothing about because hardly anyone talks about them.

Since the 19th century, much ink has been spilled in discussions over the origin of the lunar craters. Because science often advances by comparing with what already exists, scientists chose one of following possibilities to determine how the craters were formed.

• Natural methods:
   —By volcanic activity (by analogy with the craters of terrestrial volcanoes)
   —By meteoric impact (by analogy with terrestrial examples such as Meteor Crater)
   —By the collapse of a subterranean cavity (a dissolved pocket, a cavern, or underground quarries)

• Methods originating in living things:
   —By mechanical activity linked to an intelligent life form (explosives or machines, such as those used in open-sky mining)
   —By the activity of an extraterrestrial organism

It is also possible to imagine big bacteria devouring the rock and moving around, leaving traces comparable to lava from volcanoes, just as on Earth the larva of an ant lion creates a crater to capture ants and throws sand off all around.

While on Earth, the five possibilities coexist without any problem, where the Moon is concerned, scientists seem to have rejected the last three out of hand and have divided themselves between the "pro-impact" and "pro-volcanism" camps. The partisans of meteorite impacts have ended by carrying the day. That is rather astounding because absolutely nothing prevents the coexistence of different types of craters on Earth. So why not on the Moon? Why have scientists sought to retain only one explanation when the solution could be linked to the combination of different types of possible craters?

It could in fact be the case that thousands of meteorites fell on the Moon when its crust was still "viscous." The meeting of different shock waves might be the origin of certain polygonal forms observed.

Even so, I did come across an attempt to explain polygonal craters by the great volcanologist, Haroun Tazieff. The tone of the following text gives some idea of the struggles between the "pro-impact" and "pro-volcano" camps:[48]

> *The hypothesis officially accepted according to which the lunar "craters" are due to the impacts of gigantic meteorites is, to my mind, erroneous. Not that there aren't impact craters on our satellite, far from it, but a far greater number much more plausibly represent the upper face, set for all time, of thermal convection cells that stirred the magma of which the Moon was composed when it was still completely fluid.*
>
> *Those who hold that the craters originated from impacts have never been able to answer the question of why a crater resulting from the fall of a meteorite, instead of being circular, would be polygonal in form. But it is known, since the work by Bénard on the phenomenon of thermal convection in fluids, that convection cells in simultaneous*

activity and pressed next to one another, pass from the cylindrical form that characterizes isolated cells to that of a polyhedral right-angled prism, with hexagonal bases when the viscosity is sufficient.

This would also be the case in the juxtaposition of two or more lunar craters that is commonly observed. While this is easily accounted for by the magma convection hypothesis, <u>the impact hypothesis can, on this point, only remain silent</u>. The same applies to the diminution of the diameters of craters that overlap. In my opinion it stems from the diminishing depth of these cells as viscosity grows, which is linked to the cooling process.

A quarter of a century ago, the debate was lively between the supporters of the impact theory and those of the convective school (often named "volcanic"). <u>The specialists at NASA being mostly "pro-impact," and the prestige of NASA (as well as that of the United States) having impressed, as usual, the scientific flock as well as the general public, the meteoritic hypothesis was finally accepted by acclaim without having taken into account the three questions recalled above. It is too often the custom in the scientific microcosm to not give any answer to embarrassing questions and simply ignore them</u>. The fact that this attitude conflicts with ethics does not seem to bother the average scientist in the least. And today, everyone, or almost everyone, considers the Moon's craters to have been engendered by impact, although most of them seem to me to be linked to the tremendous volcanism of the Moon's early years.[49]

For many craters, Tazieff is surely right, but for those that are isolated and polygonal, such as the one in the photograph below, there could be another hypothesis—the form could very well have come about artificially due to the activity of machines. Some sort of mining activity.

It is difficult to believe and yet look at the photos below:

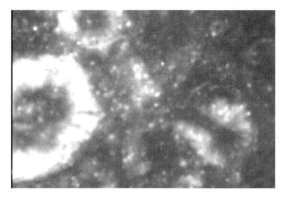

(Clementine photograph, NASA)

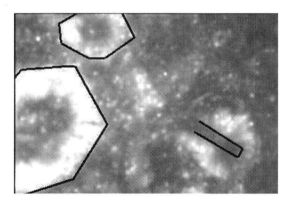

Anomalies highlighted

Note that the external boundary of the first crater forms a six-sided polygon. Also, it is not in contact with any other craters. If it is easy to understand that lava bubbles touching one another have a flat contact surface; it is much more difficult to explain why an isolated crater would become polygonal.

As for the second crater with an almost straight black trench, its appearance may be due to lava that flowed in the interior, but I do not see how a meteorite could have dug out such a crater.

Ukert is a triangular, and thus polygonal, crater, well-known to

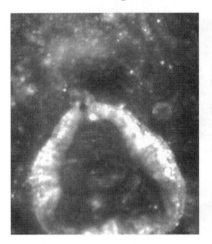 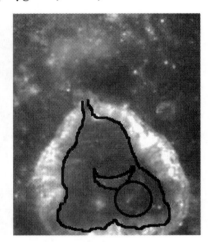

Ukert Crater (Clementine photograph, NASA) (Latitude +7 Longitude +1)   *Anomalies highlighted*

astronomers. It is difficult to accept that a meteorite could cause such a crater since the result of an explosion could not be triangular.

A close look at the interior of this crater reveals things like rocks in the form of a crescent and, in the bottom right-hand corner, a sort of crown of linked domes. I would like to find a geologist who could explain how a meteorite is capable of leaving an impact like that.

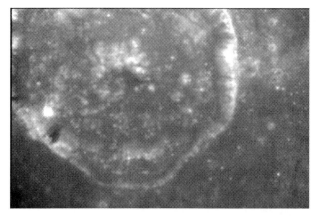

Manilius Crater (Clementine photograph, NASA)
(Latitude +14 Longitude +10)

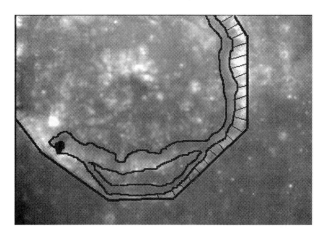

Anomalies highlighted

The upper part of the Manilius Crater is circular, but it is the only part that is. This photograph shows that:[50]

* The lower part of the crater has a very clear polygonal appearance;

- The bottom of the talus is lower than the bottom of the crater, as if the outline was dug out before they started on the central part. Moreover, the scooping out of the central part is unfinished, judging by the big groove visible in the lower portion of the crater;
- The black spot on the left, at the end of the big groove looks like a deeper hole. Could it be the entrance to a cavern?

Manilius Crater seen by Lunar Orbiter
Detail of photograph 4-97H2

This photograph is older than the one taken by the Clementine probe, and the entrance to the "cavern" is invisible. Also note the unusual arrangement of ejections, which tend to go off in straight lines at a tangent to the crater. According to the meteorite theory, the ejections should be arranged in a crown around the crater. But this is far from it.

Do you think this relief is that of a meteoric impact (the

NASA hypothesis), a volcanic crater (Haroun Tazieff's hypothesis), or an ancient open-sky mine (hypothesis of extraterrestrial mining activity)? I favor the third hypothesis, especially because no machines are visible.

To finish with the topic of volcanic and meteoritic theories, let us look at a series of photos showing anomalies that could never have occurred naturally. Another explanation needs to be found.

Works in the Craters

Here are some anomalies observed in or nearby craters. "Nature" seems to have wanted to do a little too much. Remember that these are all supposed to be the result of a collision with a meteor.

(Clementine photograph, NASA)Artificial trenches?   *Anomalies highlighted*

This shows two parallel trenches that have been dug on or below this crater's talus. The lunar surface appears to have been "clawed" over a long distance (one pixel = 260 ft.). Fix in your memory the imprint in the form of a knife blade visible in the upper part of the crater because you will find it again in another photograph in this book.

Are the official theories able to explain such marks within a crater?[51] No, of course not, because even a meteorite arriving laterally would not have left such a trace. The rubble from the cutting is perfectly distributed on both sides of the trenches. Too bad for the meteorite theory, but artificial activity would explain such markings in a crater better.

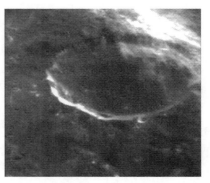

Suspect notches? (Clementine photograph, NASA)

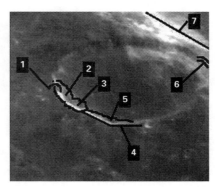

Anomalies highlighted

Several startling things can be seen in the photographs above. They show an old crater that is very circular, without any signs of ejections. The crater has a magnificent flat bottom that is incompatible with a meteoritic impact because it lacks any central blister. At the eight o'clock position, there are two new notches on the edge of the crater (2 and 3): one resembling a meteorite impact (3), and one not (2). At the bottom of the second notch (2), towards the nine o'clock position, there is a curved object (1) formed of four juxtaposed balls that stand like some sort of conduit for evacuating rubble. In neither case is there a trace of the projection of matter onto the surrounding darker ground.

Now look at the white circular line (5) which starts at the small crater at eight clock and joins other lines. It runs along the old crater wall of which some faces have a tendency to become octagonal (4). There is even what looks like reinforcements on the wall (6).

Other lines are tangential to the ancient crater. There is also a beautiful trace of a landslide (7) at the top right.

Could these lines not be the dust of freshly extracted ore rather than the result of projects from the impact of a meteorite?

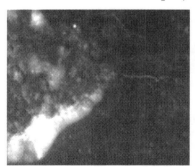
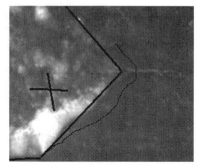

Works in progress?
(Clementine photograph,
NASA)

Anomalies highlighted

I don't know if the crater shown above is in the middle of being dug or being filled in, but there is a big X straddling the crater's talus (center left of the photograph). This X-shaped object seems to be composed of several modules. Could it be a machine?

The polygonal shape of this crater in formation is very clear, and there is the trace of an outline on the surface which may indicate the future limit of the crater's edge.

Birt Craters (Clementine photograph, NASA)
(Latitude –23.5 Longitude 352)

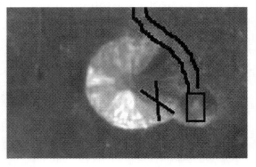

Anomalies highlighted

The anomaly here almost resembles a bridge over the little crater.[52] There appears something abnormal about the smaller Birt crater. Also, it seems to be some sort of platform in it.

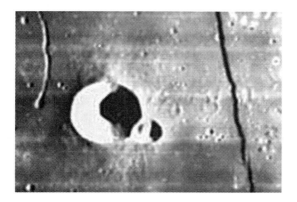

Photograph taken by Lunar Orbiter

It looks almost as if someone placed a lump of sugar in a funnel. There is also a trace that begins at the Noon position of the little crater in the direction of the Noon position of the big crater. In the big crater, a sort of X is visible, one of whose branches contradicts the lines of ejection from any impact.

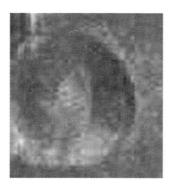

Detail of the anomaly

There are other different photographs of the Birt craters posted at the Clementine Web site. Be sure to have a look at it.

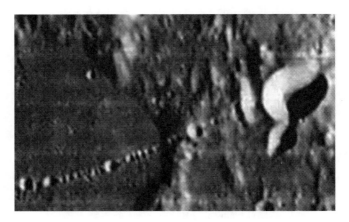

Stitches (detail of a photograph taken by Lunar Orbiter 5)
Reference 4-108H2

This looks like a fault covered by bridges, reminiscent of a stitched-up wound. It might also be a line of craters even if the probability of such a formation is small. This would be a good place for a future probe to land.

What should be done when the observed facts fit badly with the official theory? Proposing a new theory at the risk of being branded a madman who's watched too many episodes of *X-Files* is far from easy, but it's the only conceivable solution for the moment. The scientists seem to have opted for silence. But let's continue to voice our concerns.

Lunar Objects

Here are some unidentified lunar objects caught red-handed by the Clementine probe. How can the presence of such objects on our satellite be explained? Since their size is gigantic, it cannot be a question of human technology. That is surely why Frank Borman uttered the phrase: "Please be informed that there is a Santa Claus."

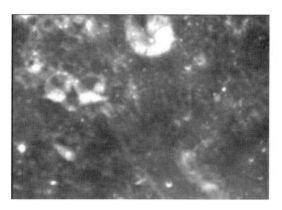

Parallel-shaped object in action?
(Clementine photograph, NASA)
(Latitude −30 Longitude +300)

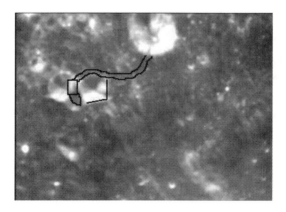

Anomalies highlighted

Look at the parallel-shaped object situated at the center of the three small craters above. Its shadow and the trace of its movement are indicated on the photograph highlighting anomalies. It does not seem that it could have arrived before the impacts.

How can such an object remain in balance at this spot? Could it be some sort of tipper used for the transport of ore or a platform? Judging by the trace connecting the craters, wouldn't you say that it had moved from one to the other?

It is also possible that this object is involved with the origin of the two craters, one of which is beginning to take a polygonal form. When it has finished gnawing out the central part, the final crater will probably resemble the one at the top center of the photo.

The same kind of object can be found in another photograph taken by the Clementine study.

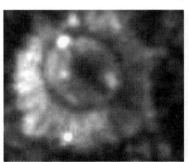 

Object and circular trace (Clementine photograph, NASA)

Lunar Orbiter also photographed a similar object in a small crater

The parallel-shaped object seems to have come from elsewhere. The trail of its path is impressive, and the circular trace at the bottom of the crater is superb. These are enough to demolish the existing theories of crater formation.

Detail of photograph 4-108H2 taken by Lunar Orbiter (NASA)

The object in question almost resembles a big insect. Is it responsible for the fact that the upper part of this crater tends to be polygonal?

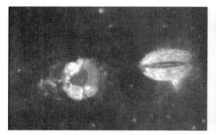 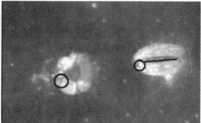

Messier Craters (Clementine photograph, NASA)   *Anomalies highlighted*

Messier's name is given to two famous craters. Observe the "balls" attached to the walls of both at the eight o'clock position. How do they maintain themselves there, taking into account the slope?

The oval crater is strange, indeed. Where are the ejections that should be visible at the sides where the explosion was strongest? And what is the cause of that nice white line at the bottom of the crater?

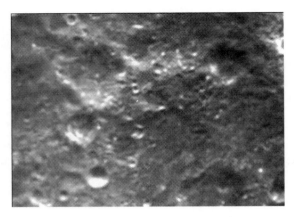

Remnants? (Clementine photograph, NASA)

The Tycho Crater is just to the right of this photo. Southwest of the triangular crater at the upper right, there is something like beams about 2.5 mi. long that form a grill and, just above these slightly to the right, an unknown structure. They look like pearls of diminishing size forming an upside-down V. At each end of the V is a bigger pearl.

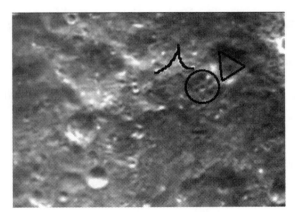

Anomalies highlighted

Here is the same spot viewed by the Lunar Orbiter a few years earlier.

Detail of a photograph by Lunar Orbiter (NASA)
See 4-124H2 and other photographs of Tycho

To finish with the topic of the strange assortment of objects visible in the craters, here is a good photo taken by the Apollo 16 during its passage over the hidden face of the Moon.

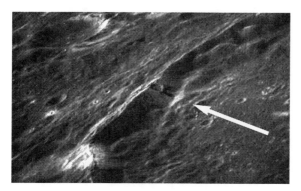

Lobachevsky Crater
Apollo 16 mission photograph (NASA)
(Latitude 10,0 N, Longitude 111, 6 E)

At the center of the photograph, there is an object in the form of an obelisk projecting a straight-lined shadow on the wall of Lobachevsky Crater. This is an original place to install a tower, chimney, or antenna. Or else it is a particularly exceptional natural feature.

Traces of Movement

What could be more natural for unidentified lunar objects than to leave identifiable traces of their movements? Here are some of the best examples among them.

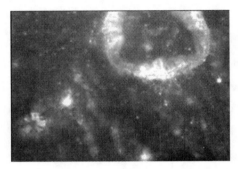

Straight-lined trace, Ukert Crater (Clementine photograph, NASA)
(Latitude +7, Longitude +1)

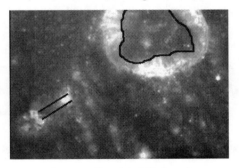

Anomalies highlighted

An important feature is the straight-lined trace running from the small crater at the bottom left towards the Ukert Crater. Something has moved from one crater to the other, hugging the ground relief and leaving behind a nice track of constant width on the lunar surface. Since when did a meteorite leave traces of movement on the Moon's face?

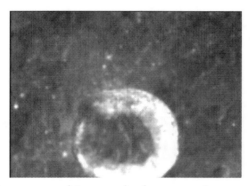

A strange object at the bottom of a crater?
(Clementine photograph, NASA)

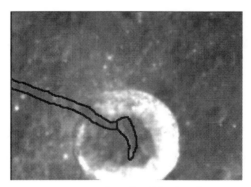

Anomalies highlighted

What is interesting here is that there is an "object" in the shape of a knife blade at the bottom of this crater. There are traces of a slide, as if the object came from elsewhere. The track is far too regular to be that of lava. This object is similar to the imprint in the form of a knife blade seen previously above two trenches in another crater. What is worse, the object and the print appear to be the same size, although the craters were not the same.

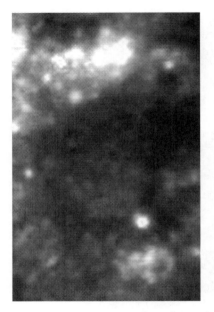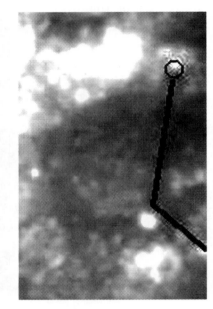

An object in movement?
(Clementine photograph, NASA)

Caught in the act by the cameras of the Clementine probe, an "object" nearly 3,500 ft. wide has left a trace of its movement on the lunar surface. Close observation shows that it turns through 60 degrees when it reaches the white dot situated at the bottom right of the photograph. Skeptics will see only a rock that has rolled along the lunar surface, but this type of anomaly is fairly frequent. In the book, *Somebody Else Is on the Moon,* there is a photograph taken by NASA[53] which seems to correspond to two rolling objects at the bottom of Vitello Crater. One of the objects had climbed the crater wall.

Parallel traces (Lunar Orbiter photograph, NASA)
Detail of photograph 4-131H3

If these traces are due to a separation of the lunar crust:
- Why are they of consistent width and depth over hundreds of miles?
- Why do they hug the lunar relief rather than splitting it in two?
- Is it possible that they are due to one or more machines scraping the lunar surface?

Extraterrestrial Bases

Certain lunar craters are so complex that the photographs resemble aerial views of military bases. Here are geometric structures beside the most polygonal crater wall. Are they natural or artificial?

Gassendi Crater
Detail of the photograph 4-143H2
taken by Lunar Orbiter (NASA)

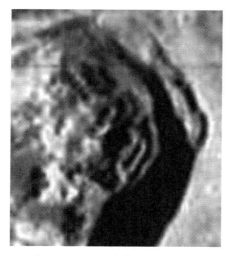

Enlargement of the small crater

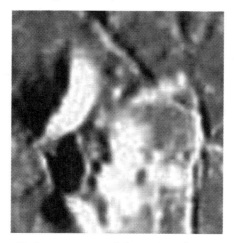

Enlargement of the central area

The black area between the two white rocks is most intriguing. It resembles a sort of plate set vertically. The edge stands out above the shadow.

Here is the same crater viewed by the Clementine satellite in 1994.

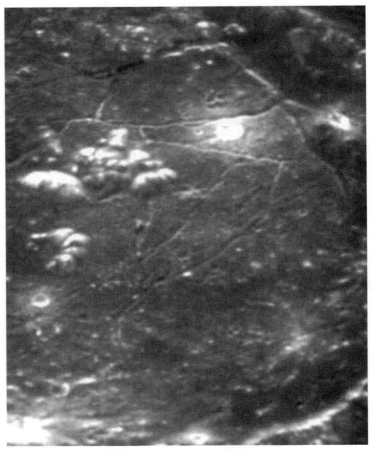

An extraterrestrial base?
(Clementine photo, NASA)
(Latitude –18, Longitude 320

An enlargement allows the identification of six different elements.

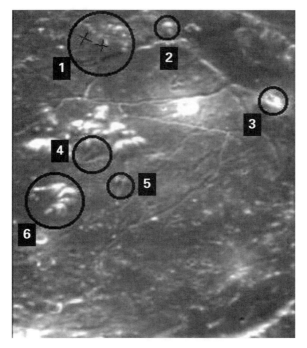

An extraterrestrial base (anomalies highlighted)

1. Two crosses drawn on the wall overlooking a fissure (The "object" within the fissure is rocks in the form of aligned domes)
2. A big rock in the form of a dome
3. An "object" emerging from small white crater.
4. A triangular "object" between the rocks, just in front of the plate photographed by Lunar Orbiter
5. The track on the surface ends at one of the blocks, as if created by it
6. A big rock in the form of a crescent (already observed in Ukert Crater)

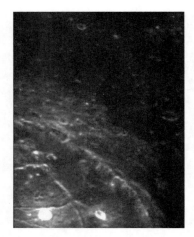

Trails (Clementine photo, NASA)

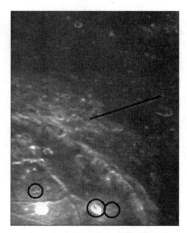

Anomalies highlighted

In this other photograph, the "object" within the white spot on the right is still visible. It is located near the holes in the wall above the white spot on the left and further above, the big rock in the form of a dome. There is a triangle visible to the right of the white spot containing the object and a luminous one-directional ray leaving a small crater (outside the bigger one).

Here is another example of what one can find in lunar craters:

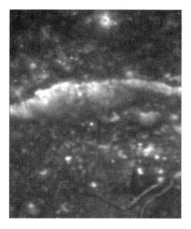

A lunar city? (Clementine photograph, NASA)

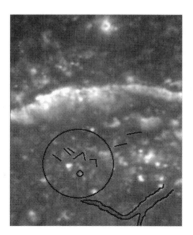

Anomalies highlighted

This photograph is scattered with small spheres of identical sizes and regular straight or right-angled forms. Could they be habitations? Other forms resemble rollers placed on the ground.

Can one really conclude that these are natural forms? How can scientists have seen such photographs and not asked themselves questions? In any case, this photograph is reminiscent of the aerial view of a city.

Notice the perfect form of the triangle separating the two channels. At a time when the mere orientation of stones on Mars permits one to determine the presence of water, what are we to make of this channel that divides into two branches?

The French astronomer Camille Flammarion saw factories on the Moon. Well, so do I.

Strange Rays

Another great mystery about the Moon is the white rays. Readily visible with binoculars on nights when there is a full moon, some of them (like the one running from Tycho to Messier) are over 1,200 mi. long.

To understand what is happening, imagine a mortar shell falling on a sandy beach. During the explosion, a large part of the sand expelled falls all around the place where the crater is formed.

The explanation retained by scientists is that these are ejecta.[54] Ejecta are said to be "crowned" when they are more or less circular around the crater. In fact, the "crowned" form is standard for all meteoritic ejecta.

However, this explanation does not fit the observed facts because, on the Moon, certain ejecta leave in a straight line while keeping a constant width over hundreds of miles. Others avoid certain directions.

Here is a good example:

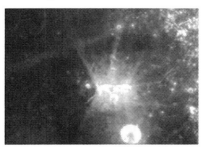

Strange ejecta (Clementine photo, NASA)
(Latitude +22, Longitude 29)

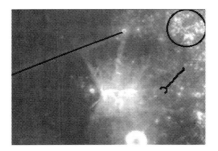

Anomalies highlighted

Much can be learned by looking closely at the white ray leaving in a straight line from the little crater at the top of the photograph. Here is an explanation given by George Leonard in his book, *Somebody Else Is on the Moon,* that is the most practical even if it seems extreme in its conclusions:

The flying objects almost always land in the interior and at the bottom of the big craters whose surface is covered in fine white dust. These vehicles constantly circulate between the craters, bringing or taking away things or beings. The fine white dust has the particularity of sticking to the shell of these flying vehicles. At takeoff, at landing, and in full flight, these vehicles are subjected to vibrations and shaking that cause this film of dust to fall off. Due to the fact that these flying vehicles follow fixed, straight-line itineraries, dust falls along these fixed trajectories. When one is dealing with craters where intense activity is going on, the flying objects take flight and come into land, in and from all directions. In the case of more specialized craters or ones with less traffic, the flight corridors are only oriented in one or two directions.

This is a long way from the "crowned" form advocated by the meteoritic theory. That said, no flying devices are visible either.

According to the *Encyclopaedia Universalis,* the phenomenon of "rapidly" vanishing ejecta is a property of the solar wind. Thus, this trace is constituted by "relatively" recent dusts.

There is a sort of Y-shaped pipeline to the right of the luminous spot at the center of the photograph and another to its left in the area mysteriously avoided by the rays. By looking attentively at the structure in the upper right-hand corner, several series of domes placed in lines can be observed. How can

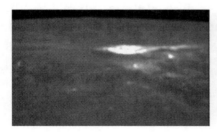 

New and ancient rays   Anomalies highlighted
(Clementine photo, NASA)

one explain such anomalies without reference to machines flying overhead that exceed anything in our technology?

As was explained in the previous discussion, the solar wind has the property of tarnishing the ejecta "rapidly." The *Encyclopaedia Universalis* does not specify how quickly this occurs, but that question is primordial, in my opinion, because an answer would make it possible to date the anomalies witnessed on the Moon. In this photograph, a very white crater with an ancient crown of grayish ejecta and a white trail leaving in a straight line from the crater can be seen. If the action of the solar wind has a tendency to turn the deposits of white dust gray, then we have irrefutable proof that there exist comings and goings of spacecraft on our satellite. How else is the difference in tint between the ancient gray ejecta and crater to be explained?

Only a recent mining operation exposing naked rock could have restored its shine. The white trail is only made of new dust that is spread after the ore is loaded. That is why the ray only runs in one direction.

The same is also shown by this photograph taken of another crater:

One-directional ejecta equals works in the craters

If ejecta are involved, what explains the presence of white dust when the crater walls are gray? An ejectum the same age as the crater should be the same color.

And why is this dust only deposited in a single direction, towards the top of the picture? What do you think? (You must admit that the theory of space vessels spreading dust along their paths seems seductive.)

I would like to see scientists try an experiment in accelerated aging on the powder of Moon rocks. All it would take would be to place it in vacuum and expose it to a source simulating the solar wind. Assuming that it might require less than a 1000 years to go from white to gray, we could have the proof that the mining operations were "recent."

Unidentified Rolling Objects

And to end this study, here is an example of "disinformation by omission" performed by NASA[55] (with a photo of the Lunar Orbiter 5 probe):

Downslope boulder trail

Description

The picture from Lunar Orbiter 5 shows a rock (just to the right of the center of the photo) that rolled and slid down a slope leaving a trail on the lunar surface. It is situated in Vitello Crater and shows the small roll that weak gravity has on the lunar surface. The principal source of modification of the lunar surface remains the bombardment of meteorites and micro-meteorites. This photograph covers 16 km (10 mi.) in the vertical direction, and North is located at the top."[56]

Critical Analysis

Judging by NASA's commentary, it is a matter of "move along, there's nothing to see"—at least nothing more than a rock that fell down a slope, leaving a trail in the lunar dust. But there are several anomalies showing that what is there cannot be a rock. Why does NASA not talk about them in its commentary? Is this an oversight or is it deliberate?

For starters, do not be satisfied with the low resolution photo below.

Boulder on the Moon

Important details don't show up in it. Download the same photograph in high resolution and store it on your hard drive where software like Paintshop Pro will permit you to "zoom" on the interesting parts.

What exactly can be observed? Not only one, but two objects (No. 1 and 2) that have left traces of movement on the lunar surface can be seen. Given the scale dimensions of the photo cited above by NASA, it can be deduced that object No. 1 covered over four mi., while object No. 2 covered almost six mi. It measures almost 800 ft. in diameter or width, while object No. 2 is about 160 ft. wide. The traces left on the surface correspond to the diameter or width of the objects, which seems impossible if they were spherical in shape.

Test this yourself. Take a billiard ball and dip it in ink, then release it on an inclined surface. The contact surface of a sphere is always less than its diameter, unless the sphere is sunk into the surface up to the depth of its radius. Have you ever seen a spherical boulder 800 ft. in diameter advancing over four mi. while penetrating 400 ft. into the surface?

In this photo, the traces have a constant width and seem much less deep than the radius of the objects. The logical deduction is that these two objects are not spherical. This impression is reinforced because only one face of the object is in shade under lateral lighting. They resemble conical objects rather than spheres.

Here are two unidentified objects that have covered a great distance across the Moon. Object No. 2 has left the little crater at the top of the photo. (Its trace within the rectangle is clearly visible.) It would seem that it has climbed up the steep, internal talus of the small crater before continuing outside for over five mi. This is strange behavior for a boulder.

I would like the scientists who made fun of me when I said to them that certain lunar craters were probably artificial in origin, to explain how a boulder 160 ft. in diameter could climb the internal slope of a crater? The trail of object No. 1 is crossed by an object that resembles some kind of "pipe," linking two craters (see the inset arc). This could only have been "installed" after the passage of object No. 1, because it covers the latter's trail. If this were not the case, the object would have been stopped by this natural barrier or crushed it. It could also have had a trampoline effect with a momentary interruption of the trail. The diameter of the pipe is about 320 ft. for a length of about two mi.

I also asked myself the following questions:

- Why haven't the other "boulders" visible in this photo moved from their positions? A moonquake or a meteorite impact should have caused more of them to roll.
- Why hasn't the big "boulder" shattered into several pieces during its displacement?
- Why do the trails of the two objects fail to follow the natural slopes of the terrain? In fact they advance almost like a skier would—perpendicular to the slope of the terrain.
- Why are the trails almost parallel despite the fact that they are separated by about four mi.?

It is impossible that the NASA specialists could have failed to notice these anomalies. So what are we supposed to believe when they explain to us that it is just a boulder? And what are the amateur and professional astronomers doing? Why have they accepted this version without reacting?

Here is the latest information from Arnaud Delaunay:

Certain NASA sites contradict the 16 km scale given for the photo of the objects. At http://www.hq.nasa.gov/office/pao/-history/TM3487/ch12-1.htm *paragraph 350, is the following text:* "[350] [PICTURE MISSING] Lunar Orbiter V photographed an area in the Vitello crater (south of Marche Humorum at 30.61 degrees South latitude, 37.57 degrees West longitude) on August 17, 1967. The enlarged portion of that high-resolution telephoto picture reveals two large "rolling stones," whose paths are clearly visible. The larger one near the center of the picture is about 23 m. across and has rolled or bounced some 274 m. The smaller rock is 4.6 m. across and has traveled 365 m."

The objects in question are only 75 ft. and 14 ft. across. Is this disinformation designed to make people lose all interest in the study of these objects or an error in scale at the other Web site?

A closer investigation was carried out to determine the true size of the objects. If they proved to be big, that would be formal proof that they were artificial.

On this subject, here is the response from Dave Williams (NASA), author of the Web page, *http://nssdc.gsfc.-nasa.gov/imgcat/html/object_page/lo5_h168_2.html*. "It looks like 16 km is correct, although I admit that it makes for a mighty large (250 m/) boulder."

And then, three days later, after asking for verication, he wrote:

It looks like the lower caption is correct, five and 25 m. is right. The image is a detail of the original image, which I assumed was the full image. I haven't actually been able to find the part of the full image the detail comes from, but I believe the caption must be referring to the same boulder tracks.

It is astonishing to see that the author of the Web site has started to ask questions about the boulder. Why did he not notice anything unusual when he created his page? How can NASA specialists commit such errors? Why did Dave Williams not rectify his first page?[57]

Summary of Anomalies Observed

- Polygonal form (triangle, hexagon, octagon) of certain craters
- Trails of constant width going from one crater to another
- Unknown "objects" in or nearby craters (parallelepipeds or Xs)
- Craters being formed
- One-directional ejecta with constant widths
- Tangential ejecta
- Ejecta running from the interior of the crater
- Domes attached to the walls or lines of domes
- Very white craters with crowns of grayish ejecta
- Grooves and parallel traces on the surface
- Rocks in the form of crescents
- Stitches or bridges across a fault

That represents a fairly big dose of anomalies that are inexplicable by the official theories ("pro-impact" or "pro-volcano") If one adds the TLPs described in Chapter Two, the conclusions of the *Cometa Report,* and the conversations of the astronauts, one obtains a coherent overview which tends to point towards an extraterrestrial presence on the Moon.

I warned you. You will never see the Moon with the same eyes again.

Possible Alternative Conclusions

What would be the most rational explanation for such phenomena? Immense pockets of volcanic gas could exist under the lunar crust. "Leaks" of this gas would lift up enormous amounts of lunar dust. The sunlight striking the gas and the dust cloud would give birth to these strange phenomena visible from Earth.

Here again, it is possible to imagine various conclusions.

Hypothesis No. 1: Imagination

Science does not have to account for this hypothesis to explain certain anomalies. It maintains that all the anomalies visible in the lunar craters are of natural origin (volcanic or meteoritic). Even if the polygonal form of some craters may give rise to confusion, one day their natural origin will be proved. The same applies to one-directional ejecta with constant widths. We can imagine seeing animals in the clouds, so why not construction in the lunar craters?

We have to come back down to reality and remind ourselves of the judicious advice furnished on a Web site devoted to Transient Lunar Phenomena.[58]

> *In no case should you let your imagination exceed the resolution power of your instrument. If Camille Flammarion saw factories on the Moon, R. Baker saw vegetation, and*

others saw bridges, tunnels, highways, and even the Great Wall of China, avoid having similar visions of this nature. Don't forget that the observation of an important astronomical phenomenon demands seriousness and objectivity. The scientific rigor necessary for the study of these surprising phenomena is not satisfied by ideological fantasies, which consists in uncovering at any price, and everywhere, little green men, or, if you prefer, hoodwinking themselves.

In other words, the Moon is only a sterile desert, whether all the dreamers like it or not. The extraterrestrials, if they exist at all, are too far away to pay us a visit.

Hypothesis No. 2: Extraterrestrials

The conquest of the Moon was mainly a military enterprise designed to verify if UFOs represent a menace to our Earth. The cooperation between the Russians and Americans stemmed from this discovery.

It is very likely that the lunar craters have been the object of a gigantic mining operation that took place in ancient times and still continues today. The debris of meteorites or the composition of the rocks probably interest the extraterrestrials unless they are repairing the hull of their enormous space vessel placed in orbit around the Earth. Certain craters are surely artificial in origin, but most are natural craters that have been modified.

The one-directional rays beside numerous craters are not linked to ejecta that followed impacts but to the over-flights of devices scattering fresh dust in their wake. By involuntarily jettisoning fresh, hence whiter, dust in their comings and goings, these machines end up creating figures resembling the projection of matter. The craters that do not have such rays have been abandoned long enough for the white dust to become tarnished due to solar radiation and then disappear.

Hypothesis No. 3: Humans

This is a variation on hypothesis No. 2. The difference is that the extraterrestrials are, in reality, humans descended from an ancient race (e.g., Atlantis) that reached a very advanced level of technology. They constructed or redesigned the Moon by taking materials from Earth. It is a sort of immense orbital station. The UFOs serve to come down to Earth and restock raw materials and food.

Critical Analysis

In order to explain these TLPs, the hypothesis of intelligent extraterrestrial activity in the lunar craters seems quite reasonable. What activity? Perhaps a large-scale mining operation, which could very well produce effects that would account for these observations. Why, after all, discard the hypothesis of non-human activity by refusing any serious analysis? Especially when confronted by the "naturally impossible" form of certain polygonal craters.[59]

Final Remarks

It seems that the company which sells plots of land on the Moon[60] is commercializing something that does not belong to it.

It is impossible to get angry with a budding "Camille Flammarion" for seeing artificial craters on the Moon, even if science one day proves definitively that these are natural anomalies. In contrast, it is possible to have a grievance with "extreme rationalists" for having seen only natural craters if one day we find out some of them were artificial.

Imagination should be the motor of science. To voluntarily exclude hypotheses by starting from the precept that man is the only form of intelligent life in the universe is no longer science. It is religion.

Internet Links on the Same Subjects

Sites on extraterrestrial phenomena

In English:

VGL Home Page—

http://www.vgl.org

The Martian Enigmas Home Page—

http://www.psrw.com/~Markc/Marshome.html

Malta UFO Research—

http://www.mufor.org

Anomalous Images and UFO Files—

http://www.Anomalous-images.com/

Digital Lunar Orbiter Photographic Atlas of the Moon (high resolution pictures)—

http://www.lpi.usra.edu/research/lunar_orbiter/

It is important to look at the two photos of Bullialdus Crater. In them, the triangular craters, as well as "objects" in the craters, are easy to distinguish.

In French:

Clementine Mission Web Site—
http://clementine.cnes.fr

Who's Already on the Moon?—
http://www.geocities.com/CapeCanaveral/Launchpad/4629/index.htm

Sites about TLPs

In English:

Lunar transient Phenomena sites—
www.ltpresearch.org/manual/chap4.html

The Lunascan Project (TLP)—
www.astrosurf.com/lunascan/-ltppage.htm
www.mufor.org/tlp/lunar.html and

The most complete: Nasa Technical Report R-277.

In French:

Transient Lunar Phenomena—
http://www.astrosurf.com/sirius/ptl1.html

This is an excellent article.

Luxorion—
www.astrosurf.com/lombry/ltp.htm

APPENDIX

Table of Transient Lunar Phenomena

Date & Time	Feature or Location; Duration	Description	Observer	Reference
Jan 6, 1960	Alphonsus	Red spot	Warner	J. Int. Lunar Soc. 1960
Nov, 1960	Piton; ~30 min	Red obscuration concealing peak	Schneller	Cameron 1965
Dec 1, 1960	Piton	Red obscuration less intense than in September	Schneller	Cameron 1965
Jan, 1961	Piton	Red obscuration less intense than in September	Schneller	Cameron 1965
Feb 15, 1961 ~08h11m	Aristarchus, Plato	Seen as bright features during solar eclipse (on film of eclipse shown by BBC May 6, 1966)	Sartory, Middlehurst	Contrib. by Middlehurst
May 30-31, 1961	Aristarchus	Enhancement of spectrum in UV	Grainger, Ring	Grainger and Ring 1963
Jun 27-28, 1961	Aristarchus, ray near Bessel	Enhancement of spectrum in UV	Grainger, Ring	Grainger and Ring 1963
Jun 29-30, 1961	E of Plato	Enhancement of spectrum in UV	Grainger, Ring	Grainger and Ring 1963
Oct 18, 1961	Eratosthenes	Bright spot in crater	Bartlett	Strol. Astr. 1962

Date & Time	Feature or Location; Duration	Description	Observer	Reference
Nov 26, 1961	Aristarchus region	Red glow seen Anomalous spectra in red and blue	Kozyrev	Kozyrev 1963
Nov 28, 1961	Aristarchus region	Red glow seen Anomalous spectra in red and blue	Kozyrev	Kozyrev 1963
Dec 3, 1961	Aristarchus region	Red glow seen Anomalous spectra in red and blue	Kozyrev	Kozyrev 1963
Sept 5, 1961	Region of Walter near terminator; 7 min	Faint point of light	Chalk	Cameron 1965
Sep 16, 1961	"Whole moon"	Spectrum showed UV emission, particularly in region of H and K lines by comparison with spectra of Sun, Mars and Jupiter	Spinrad	Spinrad 1964
Oct 8, 1962	Aristarchus; ~1 hr	Activity	Adams	Cameron 1965
Oct 5, 1963	Aristarchus region	Enhancement of 30 percent at 5450 A	Scarfe	Scarfe 1965

Date & Time	Feature or Location; Duration	Description	Observer	Reference
Oct 30, 1963	Aristarchus region	Color changes; reddish-orange to ruby patches	Greenacre, Barr	Greenacre 1963
Oct 30, 1963	Cobrahead; 7 min	Brightened area, 7th to 11th mag	Budine, Farrell	Cameron 1965
Nov 1, 1963, 23h00m	Near Kepler; 20 min	Enhancement of large area in red light	Kopal, Rackham	Kopal and Rackham 1964a, 1964b
Nov 11, 1963	Aristarchus	Color changes	Jacobs	Shorthill 1963; Gree 1965, p.409
Nov 28, 1963	Aristarchus, Schroter's Valley; 1 hr 15 min	Red spots, then violet, blue haze	Greenacre, et al	Greenacre 1963
Nov 28, 1963	Cobrahead; 35 min	Pink spot on W side	TombAugust	Cameron 1965
Nov 28, 1963	Aristarchus, Anaximander; ~1 hr	Red spot in Aristarchus and also on N edge of Anaximander	W. Fisher	Cameron 1965
Dec 28, 1963, 15h55m - 16h26m	Aristarchus to Herodotus; 31 min	Extensive red area	9 students at Hiroshima, Japan	Sato 1964
Dec 29-30, 1963, 22h00m - 03h00m	Aristarchus region; 5 hr	Purplish-blue patch	Doherty and others	Contrib. by Moore

Date & Time	Feature or Location; Duration	Description	Observer	Reference
Dec 30, ~1963, 11h00m	NE limb; ~20 min	During eclipse, Anomalous reddish glow inside umbra (Lunar eclipse)	Many observers	Sky and Tel. 1964
Feb 25, 1964	Cobrahead; 3 min, Aristarchus; 1 min	Red flashes, + 12 mag	Budine	Cameron 1965
Mar 16, 1964	Aristarchus	Sudden red glow on SW rim	Lecuona	Cameron 1965
Mar 18, 1964	Aristarchus	Flash	Earl and brother	Cameron 1965
Mar 26, 1964, 00h37m	Aristarchus	Floor; blue clay color	Bartlett	Bartlett, 1967
Mar 28, 1964, 01h59m	Aristarchus	Blue-violet glare, E wall and N wall; E wall bright spot; violet tinge in nimbus	Bartlett	Bartlett 1967
Apr 22, 1964	Near Ross D	Bright spot	Cross and others	Harris 1967
Apr 26, 1964	Region of Censorinus	Surface brightening somewhat similar to Kopal-Rackham (Nov 1, 1963) event	Hopmann	Hopmann 1966

Date & Time	Feature or Location; Duration	Description	Observer	Reference
May 17, 1964	Theophilus	Crimson color on W rim, ~10 mag	Dieke	Cameron 1965
May 18, 1964, 03h55m - 05h00m	SE of Ross D; 1 hr 5 min	White obscuration moved 20 mph, Decreased in extent. Phenomenon repeated. Newtonians 8"f/7 and 9" f/7 used	Harris, Cross and others	Cameron 1965; Harris 1967
May 20, 1964	Plato; ~10 min	Strong orange-red color on W rim of crater, + 10 mag	Bartlett	Bartlett 1967
May 26, 1964, 04h22m	Aristarchus	Strong blue-violet glare, E wall and E wall bright spot; strong violet tinge in nimbus	Bartlett	Bartlett 1967
May 28, 1964, 05h38m	Aristarchus	Blue-violet glare; E wall bright spot, E, NE walls. Dark violet, nimbus	Bartlett	Bartlett 1967
Jun 6, 1964	Aristarchus area; 50 min	Spur between Aristarchus and Herodotus; red spots (glow) in Schroter's Valley	Schmidling, St.Clair, Platt	Cameron 1965

Date & Time	Feature or Location; Duration	Description	Observer	Reference
Jun 17, 1964	SE of Ross D	Moving bright spot; 2 brief obscurations of part of wall. Newtonian, 19" f/7	Cross, Harris	Harris 1967
Jun 20, 1964, 06h00m	Aristarchus	Nimbus only; dark violet hue	Bartlett	Bartlett 1967
Jun 21, 1964, 03h43m - 05h44m	S of Ross D; 2 hr, 1 min	Moving dark area Newtonian 19"	Harris, Cross, Helland	Harris 1967
Jun 23, 1964, 04h55m	Aristarchus	Blue-violet glare, NE rim; strong violet tinge in nimbus	Bartlett	Bartlett 1967
Jun 25, 1964 ~01h07m	Aristarchus	Very bright during eclipse (direct photograph, lunar eclipse)	Titulaer	Hemel en Dampkring 1967
Jun 25, 1964, 01h07m	Grimaldi	During lunar eclipse, white streak from Grimaldi toward limb	Azevado	Letter to Moore
Jun 26, 1964, 05h24m	Aristarchus	Dark violet in nimbus; pale violet on plateau Absent from crater	Bartlett	Bartlett 1967

Date & Time	Feature or Location; Duration	Description	Observer	Reference
Jun 27, 1964, 05h48m	Aristarchus	Bright blue-violet; E wall bright spot, E, NE rim. Dark violet in nimbus	Bartlett	Bartlett 1967
Jun 28, 1964, 06h44m	Aristarchus	Blue-violet glare; E wall bright spot, E, NE, N, NW walls	Bartlett	Bartlett 1967
Jun 28, 1964	S region of Aristarchus	Reddish-brown tone observed	Bartlett	Greenacre 1965
Jul 16, 1964	SE of Ross D	Temporary "hill," W 3 km diam. and shadow seen	Cragg	Harris 1967
Jul 17, 1964	Plato	Faint pink bands at base of inner W wall and on rim of N wall	Bartlett	Greenacre 1965
Jul 18, 1964	SE of Ross D	Bright area moved and shrank. Extent greater with amber filter	Harris	Cameron 1965; Harris 1967
Jul 18, 1964	Plato; some minutes	Pink tinge to W wall, 10th mag	Bartlett	Cameron 1965

Date & Time	Feature or Location; Duration	Description	Observer	Reference
Jul 28, 1964, 04h43m	Aristarchus	Blue-violet glare; E wall bright spot. Dark violet in nimbus; pale violet on plateau	Bartlett	Bartlett 1967
Jul 29, 1964, 05h50m	Aristarchus	Nimbus only; dark violet hue	Bartlett	Bartlett 1967
Jul 31, 1964, 05h28m	Aristarchus	Pale blue tint; NE, N, NW walls and floor	Bartlett	Bartlett 1967
Aug 16, 1964, 04h18m-05h20m	SE of Ross D; 1 hr, 2 min	Bright area. Condensations varying with time	Harris, Cross	Harris 1967
Aug 24, 1964, 04h22m	Aristarchus	Bright blue-violet; E wall bright spot, E, NE wall	Bartlett	Bartlett 1967
Aug 25, 1964, 04h58m	Aristarchus	Bright blue-violet; E wall bright spot, E, NE rim. Dark violet hue in nimbus	Bartlett	Bartlett 1967
Aug 26, 1964, 04h16m	Aristarchus	Blue-violet glare; E wall bright spot, E, NE rim. Dark violet hue in nimbus	Bartlett	Bartlett 1967

Date & Time	Feature or Location; Duration	Description	Observer	Reference
Aug 26, 1964	Aristarchus; ~1 hr	Red and blue bands	Gennatt, Reid	Cameron 1965
Aug 27, 1964 0437m	Aristarchus	Blue-violet glare; E wall bright spot, E, NE wall. Dark violet, nimbus; pale violet on plateaus	Bartlett	Bartlett 1967
Aug 28, 1964, 04h40m	Aristarchus	Faint blue-violet radiance, E wall bright spot and NE rim. Dark violet in nimbus	Bartlett	Bartlett 1967
Sep 18, 1964, 01h15m	Aristarchus	Craterlet, base NW wall; bluish	Bartlett	Bartlett 1967
Sep 20, 1964	Aristarchus to Herodotus	Several red spots in area	Crowe, Cross	Cameron 1965
Sep 20, 1964	SE of Ross D	Bright obscuration	Cross	Cameron 1965; Harris 1967
Sep 22, 1964, 03h03m	Aristarchus	Bright blue-violet glare; E wall bright spot and NE rim. Dark violet in nimbus	Bartlett	Bartlett 1967
Sep 22, 1964	KuNowsky; 1 hr	Red area blinked in blinker	Gillheaney, Hall, L. Johnson	Cameron 1965

Date & Time	Feature or Location; Duration	Description	Observer	Reference
Sep 23, 1964, 03h30m	Aristarchus	Blue-violet glare; E wall bright spot, E, NE, N, NW wall	Bartlett	Bartlett 1967
Sep 25, 1964, 04h05m	Aristarchus	Blue-violet glare; E wall bright spot. Dark violet on nimbus	Bartlett	Bartlett 1967
Sep 25, 1964, 04h43m	Aristarchus	Blue-violet glare; E wall bright spot. Dark violet in nimbus; pale violet on plateau	Bartlett	Bartlett 1967
Sep 26, 1964, 05h07m	Aristarchus	Moderately intense; E wall bright spot. Dark violet, nimbus	Bartlett	Bartlett 1967
Oct 19, 1964, 02h02m	Aristarchus	Strong blue tint E half of floor; blue-violet glare, base E side central peak	Bartlett	Bartlett 1967
Oct 22, 1964, 02h12m	Aristarchus	Blue-violet glare, E wall bright spot, E, NE wall. Dark violet hue in nimbus	Bartlett	Bartlett 1967

Date & Time	Feature or Location; Duration	Description	Observer	Reference
Oct 24,1964 04h02m	Aristarchus	Blue-violet glare; E wall bright spot, E, NE rim. Dark violet hue in nimbus	Bartlett	Bartlett 1967
Oct 25, 2964 04h17m	Aristarchus	Nimbus only; dark violet hue	Bartlett	Bartlett 1967
Oct 25, 1964, 04h37m	Aristarchus	Blue-violet glare; E wall bright spot, E, NE wall. Faint violet tinge in nimbus	Bartlett	Bartlett 1967
Oct 27, 1964	Alphonsus	Reddish-pink patch at base of sunlit central peak	L. Johnson, et al	Cameron 1965
Nov 14, 1964	Plato	Peak on W wall very brilliant white. At foot of peak on inner side, strong blue band was a small bright red spot immediately adjacent on SE.	Bartlett	Greenacre 1965
Nov 21, 1964, 01h57m	Aristarchus	Bright blue-violet glare; NE, N, and NW rims	Bartlett	Bartlett 1967

Date & Time	Feature or Location; Duration	Description	Observer	Reference
Nov 23, 1964, 03h29m	Aristarchus	Strong blue-violet glare; N, NE, NW walls. Dark violet, nimbus	Bartlett	Bartlett 1967
Nov 24, 1964, 04h50m	Aristarchus	Blue-violet glare, N rim. Dark violet in nimbus; pale violet N and NE of crater	Bartlett	Bartlett 1967
Dec 19, 1964	Aristarchus; 1 min	Brightened by a factor of 5	Budine, Farrell	Cameron 1965
Dec 19, 1964 ~02h35m	N/A N/A	Anomalous bright area during lunar eclipse	S. Hill and student	Hill 1966
Dec 19, 1964 ~02h35m	Edge of Marche Nubium	Photoelectric photometry showed strong Anomalous enhancement of radiation during lunar eclipse	Sanduleak, Stock	Sanduleak and Stock 1965

1965-1969

Date & Time	Feature or Location; Duration	Description	Observer	Reference
Mar 14, 1965, 07h40m	SE of Ross D	Crater wall partially obscured. Bright area. Cassegrain 12", f/15	Cross	Harris 1967
Jul 1, 1965	Aristarchus, dark side	Starlike image	Emanuel	Cameron 1965
Jul 2, 1965	Aristarchus; 1 hr 21 min	Bright spot like star on dark side, estimated mag 4	Emanuel, et al	Greenacre 1965
Jul 3, 1965	Aristarchus; ~1 hr10 min	Pulsating spot on dark side	Emanuel, et al	Greenacre 1965
Jul 4, 1965	Aristarchus; 1 hr	Bright spot, No pulsations, on dark side	Emanuel, et al	Greenacre 1965
Jul 7, 1965	Grimaldi	White streak extended toward limb	Azevado, et al	Revista Astr. 1965
Jul 8, 1965	Theophilus; 10 min	Bright spot	Cross	Cameron 1965; Greenacre 1965
Jul 9, 1965	Aristarchus; 2 hr 6 min	Starlike image	Emanuel	Cameron 1965
Jul 31, 1965	Aristarchus	Starlike image	Welch	Cameron 1965
Aug 2, 1965	Aristarchus; ~1 min	Starlike brightening, 8th to 9th mag	Bornhurst	Cameron 1965
August 3, 1965	Aristarchus; ~6 min	Starlike image, 6th to 7th mag	Bornhurst	Cameron 1965

Date & Time	Feature or Location; Duration	Description	Observer	Reference
Aug 4, 1965	Aristarchus; ~2 min	Starlike image, 6th to 7th mag	Bornhurst	Cameron 1965
Sep 3, 1965	SE of Ross D	Ridge obscured	Harris	Harris 1967
Sep 9, 1965, 13h20m	Aristarchus	Orange-red strip on floor	Presson	Contrib. by Moore
Oct 10, 1965, 06h07m	Aristarchus	Pale violet radiance; whole of W interior; dark violet, nimbus; pale violet on plateau	Bartlett	Bartlett 1967
Oct 11, 1965, 01h47m	Aristarchus	Whole crater, exclusive of S area, pale violet; dark violet in nimbus; pale violet on plateau	Bartlett	Bartlett 1967
Oct 12, 1965 02h20m	Aristarchus	Nimbus only; dark violet hue	Bartlett	Bartlett 1967
Oct 13, 1965 03h02m	Aristarchus	Pale, blue-violet tint on E wall bright spot and whole length of E wall; pale violet radiance in crater, exclusive of S region. Dark violet, nimbus	Bartlett	Bartlett 1967
Nov 15, 1965	Aristarchus	Bright spots	L. Johnson	*Phys. Today* 1966

Date & Time	Feature or Location; Duration	Description	Observer	Reference
Dec 1, 1965	N/A	Reddish glow followed by black obscuration	Evrard and others	Gingerich 1966
Dec 4, 1965, 04h25m	Ross D	Obscuration of part of rim, also bright area 7-10 km diameter, not seen on following night (04h00m - 07h30m)	Cross (Harris, Cragg on December 5)	Harris 1967
Feb 7, 1966, 01h10m	Aristarchus	Nimbus only; intense violet hue	Bartlett	Bartlett 1967
Mar 29, 1966, 21h00m	Archimedes	Floor bands brilliant	E.G. Hill	B.A.A. Lunar Sec. Circ. 1966, 1, No.6
Apr 2, 1966, 23h30m 20 min	Aristarchus; 20 min	Central peak very bright	M. Brown	B.A.A. Lunar Sec. Circ. 1966, 1, No.7
Apr 3, 1966, 23h00m	Aristarchus; 30 min	Central peak very bright	M. Brown	B.A.A. Lunar Sec. Circ. 1967, 1, No.7
Apr 12, 1966, 01h05m	Gassendi; 18 min	Abrupt flash of red settling immediately to point of red haze near NW wall. Continuous until 01h23m	Whippey	B.A.A. Lunar Sec. Circ. 1967, 2, No.5

Date & Time	Feature or Location; Duration	Description	Observer	Reference
Apr 30 – May 2, 1966	Gassendi	Red glows	Sartory, Moore, Moseley, Ringsdore	J.B.A.A. 1966; B.A.A. Lunar Sec. Circ. 1966, 1, No. 6
May 1, 1966, 21h55m - 22h45m	Aristarchus; 50 min	Red patch	Patterson	B.A.A. Lunar Sec. Circ. 1966, 1, No. 6
May 1, 1966, 22h10m	Aristarchus; 15 min	Small intense white spot NW of crater wall	M. Brown, Sartory	B.A.A. Lunar Sec. Circ. 1966, 1, Nos. 6, 7
May 27, 1966, 21h10m	Alphonsus; 50 min	Faint red patches	Sartory, Moore, Moseley	B.A.A. Lunar Sec. Circ. 1966, 1, No. 6
May 30, 1966, 20h52m	Gassendi; 7 min	Blink, orange patch and obscuration	Sartory	B.A.A. Lunar Sec. Circ. 1966, 1, No. 6
Jun 1, 1966, 03h20m	Aristarchus	Entire sunlit area of floor, bluish	Bartlett	Bartlett 1967
Jun 3, 1966, 06h10m	Aristarchus	Nimbus only, violet hue	Bartlett	Bartlett 1967
Jun 26, 1966, 04h30m - 04h40m	Alphonsus; 10 min	Absorption band (4880 +- 50A) seen in spectrum of central peak	Harris, Arriola	Harris 1967
Jun 27, 1966	Plato; 15 min	Inside SW wall of crater, blink	Hedley Robinson, Sartory	B.A.A. Lunar Sec. Circ. 1966, 1, No. 11
Jul 10, 1966, 02h00m	Triesnecker; 1 hr	Bright streak in crater	Allen	B.A.A. Lunar Sec. Circ. 1966, 1, No. 10

Date & Time	Feature or Location; Duration	Description	Observer	Reference
Aug 4-5, 1966, 22h37m - 23h30m and 02h32m - 02h58m	Plato; 53 min, 26 min	Red color, NE wall and floor	Corvan, Moseley	B.A.A. Lunar Sec. Circ. 1966, 1, No.10
Sep 2, 1966, 00h00m	Gassendi; 3 hr	Reddish patches	Moore, et al (8 observers)	B.A.A. Lunar Sec. Circ. 1966, 1, No. 10; ibid 1966, 1, No. 11
Sep 2, 1966	Alphonsus; intermittent, 1 hr 2 min	A series of weak glows; Final flash observed at 04h18m	Whippey	B.A.A. Lunar Sec. Circ. 1966, 2, 1 No. 12
Sep 3, 1966, 03h55m	Gassendi	Blinks on NE, ENE walls and SW and W of central peak	Moseley	B.A.A. Lunar Sec. Circ. 1966, 1, No. 10
Sep 25, 1966, 20h20m	Gassendi; 30 min	Reddish patches	Moore, Moseley	B.A.A. Lunar Sec. Circ. 1966, 1, No. 11
Sep 25, 1966, 23h12m	Plato; 3 min	Blinks in crater	Moseley	B.A.A. Lunar Sec. Circ. 1966, 1, No. 11
Oct 25, 1966, 03h46m	SE of Ross D	Large bright area obscuring half of crater wall. Not present Oct 24. Newtonian 19" f/7	Cross	Harris 1967

Date & Time	Feature or Location; Duration	Description	Observer	Reference
Oct 25, 1966, 22h30m	Gassendi	Red blinks, N wall	Moore, Moseley, Sartory	B.A.A. Lunar Sec. Circ. 1966, 2, No. 1
Oct 29, 1966, 00h45m - 01h30m	Copernicus, N rim; 45 min	Red spot	Walker	Walker 1966
Dec 22, 1966, 06h00m - 06h30m	Messier (W.H. Pickering); 30 min	Blinks on floors of both craters	Kelsey	B.A.A. Lunar Sec. Circ. 1967, 2, No. 4
Dec 23, 1966, 05h15m - 07h10m	Plato; 55 min	Numerous light streaks on floor, three bright spots on floor, all showed blinks	Kelsey	B.A.A. Lunar Sec. Circ. 1967, 2, No. 4
Dec 27, 1966, 06h30m - 07h05m	Gassendi; 35 min	Very faint blink on SW floor and another N of it on NW floor (observer considers observation very suspect)	Kelsey	B.A.A. Lunar Sec. Circ. 1967, 2, No. 4
Jan 21, 1967, 19h35m	Gassendi	Small blink and suspect faint colored patch in outer W wall in position of original observation of April 30, 1966	Sartory, Moore, Moseley, Duckworth, Kilburn	B.A.A. Lunar Sec. Circ. 1967, 2, No.3; ibid 1967, 2, No. 4

Date & Time	Feature or Location; Duration	Description	Observer	Reference
Feb 17, 1967, 17h47m - 18h12m	Alphonsus; 25 min	Blink just inside the SW floor of crater suspected on elevation NW of dark patch	Moore, Moseley	B.A.A. Lunar Sec. Circ. 1967, 2, No. 4
Feb 19, 1967, 20h30m - 20h40m	Alphonsus; 10 min	Bright red glow in position of suspected blink of Feb. 17, 1967. Fading by 20h37m	Moseley, Moore	B.A.A. Lunar Sec. Circ. 1967, 2, No. 4
Mar 22, 1967, 19h40m	Gassendi	Red color and blink	Moseley	B.A.A. Lunar Sec. Circ. 1967, 2, No. 5
Mar 23, 1967, 18h40m	Gassendi	Red color under S wall	Sartory, Farrant	B.A.A. Lunar Sec. Circ. 1967, 2, No. 5
Mar 23, 1967, 19h45m	Cobrahead	Red color outside SE wall	Moore, Moseley, Farrant	B.A.A. Lunar Sec. Circ. 1967, 2, No. 6
Mar 23, 1967, 19h05m - 19h55m	Aristarchus	Red glows	Sartory, Moore, Moseley	B.A.A. Lunar Sec. Circ. 1967, 2, No. 5, 6

Date & Time	Feature or Location; Duration	Description	Observer	Reference
Apr 15, 1967, 19h15m - 21h00m	Aristarchus (on dark side); 1 hr 45 min	Aristarchus very bright. Seeing very well until 21h00m UT, after which seeing too bad to continue observing. On April16 and 17, nothing special seen.	Classen	Hopmann 1967
Apr 21, 1967, 19h16m - 21h15m	Aristarchus; 1 hr 59 min	Bright points on S wall. Red patch to NE	Darnell, Farrant	B.A.A. Lunar Sec. Circ. 1967, 2, No. 7
Apr 21, 1967, 21h20m	Schroter's Valley, Cobrahead	Red color	Darnell, Farrant	B.A.A. Lunar Sec. Circ. 1967, 2, No. 7
Apr 22, 1967	Aristarchus (on bright side)	Aristarchus so bright that it could be seen with the naked eye	Classen	Hopmann 1967
May 20, 1967, 20h15m and 21h05m - 21h20m	Aristarchus; 15 min	Red spots on south rim. Moon low	Darnell	B.A.A. Lunar Sec. Circ. 1967, 2, No. 8
May 20, 1967	Gassendi	Elongated blink in crater, SW part of floor	Kelsey	B.A.A. Lunar Sec. Circ. 1967, 2, No. 8

Date & Time	Feature or Location; Duration	Description	Observer	Reference
May 29, 1967, 06h40m - 07h25m	Aristarchus; 45 min	Red-brown color	C.A. Anderson	B.A.A. Lunar Sec. Circ. 1967, 2, No. 8
Jun 18, 1967, 21h10m - 22h30m and 22h50m - 23h59m	Gassendi; 1 hr 20 min and 1 hr 9 min	Faint redness outside the NW and SW wall of Gassendi	Whippey	B.A.A. Lunar Sec. Circ. 1967, 2, No. 8
Aug 13, 1967, Sec. 21h00m	Alphonsus; 15 min	Glow in interior of crater	Horowitz	B.A.A. Lunar Circ. 1967, 2, No. 10
Sep 11, 1967, 00h32m	Marche Tranquilitaties; 8-9 sec	Black cloud surrounded by violet color	Montreal group	B.A.A. Lunar Sec. Circ. 1967, 2, No. 12
Sep 11, 1967, 00h45m	Sabine	Bright yellow flash visible a fraction of a second	Mrs P. Jean and Montreal group	B.A.A. Lunar Sec. Circ. 1967, 2, No. 12
Sep 17, 1967, 02h05m	Aristarchus	Red color observed	DelaNo	Kelsey 1967
Oct 10, 1967, 02h15m	SE of Ross D	Bright area moved 80 km/hr toward SSE and expanded as contrast reduced	Harris	Harris 1967

Date & Time	Feature or Location; Duration	Description	Observer	Reference
Oct 19, 1967, 05h00m	Kepler, Aristarchus	High moon, 19 after full, apogee. Kepler appeared at least one mag brighter than Aristarchus. On October 20 and 22 at 05h UT, relative brightness returned to Normal	Classen	Classen 1967

Endnotes

[1] *Soylent Green* is an apocalyptic film where human bodies are recycled to serve as food to other human beings.

[2] *http://nssdc.gsfc.nasa.gov/planetary/lunar/apollo.html.*

[3] Web site has since been shut down.

[4] To be found in the original French at *http://www.dna.fr/dna/bestweb/000000125.html.*

[5] Those interested should read *Secret Agenda: The United States Government Nazi Scientists,* and Project Paperclip, 1945 to 1990 by Linda Hunt (St. Martin's Press).

[6] See Pierre Durand's article, "Du nouveau sur le passé de Wernher Von Braun" [New Information on Wernher Von Braun's Past] (available at: *http://www.anti-rev.org/textes/Durand97a/.*

[7] "Albedo" is a term that designates the coefficient of light reflection.

[8] *Nowhere Else*

[9] It should be noted that, in the films, it falls back as a powder and not in little blocks compacted by the tires.

[10] The minimum speed to avoid any risk of blurring from movement without the use of a stand.

[11] *Now, That Beats All*

[12] At *http://perso.club-internet.fr/arnaudel/Payekhali/Dossiers/-Contre-analyse-04.html.*

[13] Physics Laboratory for Lasers, Atoms, and Molecules.

[14] Photo and text taken from: *http://franck.germain.free.fr/nasa/apollo.htm.*

[15] The speed needed to blur from movement when shutting without a stand.

[16] It is completely normal not to see any stars in the lunar sky. They exist but are not luminous enough to have the time to expose the film.

[17] The complete study is available at: *http://pages.infinit.net/cassini/debat_ombres.htm.*

[18] See Chapter Two concerning the Transient Lunar Phenomenon.

[19] This is confirmed by Arnaud Delaunay on his Web page: *http://perso.club-internet.fr/arnaudel/Payekhali/Dossiers/Contre-analyse-09.html.* The title of the page is called "The Photos of Controversy." It's very good work but starts out from the principal that the light-colored crater visible in the LM photo is that of the other photograph. The mystery thus remains complete.

[20] *Now, That Beats All.*

[21] *Nowhere Else.*

[22] *http://perso.club-internet.fr/arnaudel/Payekhali/Dossiers/-Contre-analyse-04.html.*

[23] A Flash 4 animation of these two photographs is available at the site: *http://www.hypnoide.com/moon/.*

[24] The best attempt at an explanation can be found on the page: *http://perso.club-internet.fr/arnaudel/Payekhali/Dossiers/-Contre-analyse-13.htm.*

[25] A digression could this result be due instead to continental drift? Could the fact that the ground on which the laser is sited slips slightly on the terrestrial surface not give rise to the illusion that the Moon is pulling away from us?

[26] *http://wwwrc.obs-azur.fr/cerga/laser/laslune/llr.htm.*

[27] To avoid skewing the results of the poll, you have the right to only one vote per computer IP address.

[28] Read the second half of this book before voting.

[29] *http://perso.wanadoo.fr/metasystems/UFOSightings.html.*

[30] Emphasis added by the author.

[31] *The Moon, Key to the Bible.*

[32] The setting of Orion in winter is marked by storms. The constellation crops up several times in the Aeneid, each time with a negative connotation.

[33] *UFOs and Defense: What We Should Be Prepared For.*

[34] In the chapter headed "Conclusions and Recommendations".

[35] *http://zetetique.ldh.org.*

[36] The French Institute of Advanced Studies in National Defense.

[37] The French National Center for Space Studies.

[38] Chapter One of this book.

[39] See Chapter Three.

[40] See Chapter Three.

[41] See the *Encyclopaedia Universalis.*

[42] When *The Cometa Report* Appeared.

[43] Transient Lunar Phenomena.

[44] Mckay, 1976.

[45] *Dieu des fourmis, Dieu des étoiles [God of Ants, God of Stars]* by Rémy Chauvin, published by Editions Le Pré aux Clercs, p. 45).

[46] *http://clementine.cnes.fr.*

[47] *www.lpi.usra.edu/research/lunar_orbiter.*

[48] Excerpt from the article, "Polémique sur un volcan" [Controversy over a Volcano], published in the special issue of the French astronomy magazine, *Ciel et Espace [Sky and Space]*, October.-December.1989.

[49] Text underlined by author.

[50] I verified this on other photographs taken by Clementine and Lunar Orbiter.

[51] *See http://gdcinfo.agg.nrcan.gc.ca/crater/paper/cratering_f.html.*

[52] *See also: http://web.tiscali.it/themoon/bisecteddomespaper.htm*

[53] (67-H-1135).

[54] An ejectum is a projection of matter linked to the impact of a meteorite. Consult the official NASA Web page *http://nssdc.gsfc.nasa.gov/imgcat/hires/lo5_h168_2.gif.*

[55] *http://nssdc.gsfc.nasa.gov/imgcat/hires/lo5_h168_2.gif.*

[56] Lunar Orbiter 5, image 168-H2, NASA.

[57] For an investigation carried out by another researcher, see: *http://www.multimania.com/boisse/artefact/index.html.*

[58] *http://www.astrosurf.com/sirius/ptl1.html.*

[59] See Chapter Three.

[60] *http://www.moonshop.com.*

Moon Landings